TALKING ABC

MAROUSHKA MONRO
on the problem pages of
years as 'agony aunt' on *Just Seventeen*. She also w...
articles, short stories and is a published poet. *Talking about Anorexia* is her first book.

Overcoming Common Problems Series

Curing Arthritis
More ways to a drug-free life
MARGARET HILLS

Curing Illness – The Drug-Free Way
MARGARET HILLS

Depression
DR PAUL HAUCK

Divorce and Separation
Every woman's guide to a new life
ANGELA WILLANS

Don't Blame Me!
How to stop blaming yourself and other people
TONY GOUGH

Everything Parents Should Know About Drugs
SARAH LAWSON

Family First Aid and Emergency Handbook
DR ANDREW STANWAY

Getting Along with People
DIANNE DOUBTFIRE

Getting the Best for Your Bad Back
DR ANTHONY CAMPBELL

Good Stress Guide, The
MARY HARTLEY

Heart Attacks – Prevent and Survive
DR TOM SMITH

Helping Children Cope with Bullying
SARAH LAWSON

Helping Children Cope with Divorce
ROSEMARY WELLS

Helping Children Cope with Grief
ROSEMARY WELLS

Hold Your Head Up High
DR PAUL HAUCK

How to Be Your Own Best Friend
DR PAUL HAUCK

How to Cope when the Going Gets Tough
DR WINDY DRYDEN AND JACK GORDON

How to Cope with Bulimia
DR JOAN GOMEZ

How to Cope with Difficult People
ALAN HOUEL WITH CHRISTIAN GODEFROY

How to Cope with Splitting Up
VERA PEIFFER

How to Cope with Stress
DR PETER TYRER

How to Cope with your Child's Allergies
DR PAUL CARSON

How to Do What You Want to Do
DR PAUL HAUCK

How to Improve Your Confidence
DR KENNETH HAMBLY

How to Interview and Be Interviewed
MICHELE BROWN AND GYLES BRANDRETH

How to Keep Your Cholesterol in Check
DR ROBERT POVEY

How to Love and Be Loved
DR PAUL HAUCK

How to Pass Your Driving Test
DONALD RIDLAND

How to Stand up for Yourself
DR PAUL HAUCK

How to Start a Conversation and Make Friends
DON GABOR

How to Stop Smoking
GEORGE TARGET

How to Stop Worrying
DR FRANK TALLIS

How to Survive Your Teenagers
SHEILA DAINOW

How to Untangle Your Emotional Knots
DR WINDY DRYDEN AND JACK GORDON

How to Write a Successful CV
JOANNA GUTMANN

Hysterectomy
SUZIE HAYMAN

Is HRT Right for You?
DR ANNE MACGREGOR

The Incredible Sulk
DR WINDY DRYDEN

The Irritable Bowel Diet Book
ROSEMARY NICOL

The Irritable Bowel Stress Book
ROSEMARY NICOL

Overcoming Common Problems Series

Jealousy
DR PAUL HAUCK

Learning to Live with Multiple Sclerosis
DR ROBERT POVEY, ROBIN DOWIE AND GILLIAN PRETT

Living Through Personal Crisis
ANN KAISER STEARNS

Living with Asthma
DR ROBERT YOUNGSON

Living with Diabetes
DR JOAN GOMEZ

Living with Grief
DR TONY LAKE

Living with High Blood Pressure
DR TOM SMITH

Making the Most of Loving
GILL COX AND SHEILA DAINOW

Making the Most of Yourself
GILL COX AND SHEILA DAINOW

Menopause
RAEWYN MACKENZIE

Migraine Diet Book, The
SUE DYSON

Motor Neurone Disease – A Family Affair
DR DAVID OLIVER

The Nervous Person's Companion
DR KENNETH HAMBLY

Overcoming Guilt
DR WINDY DRYDEN

Overcoming Stress
DR VERNON COLEMAN

The Parkinson's Disease Handbook
DR RICHARD GODWIN-AUSTEN

Sleep Like a Dream – The Drug-Free Way
ROSEMARY NICOL

Subfertility Handbook, The
VIRGINIA IRONSIDE AND SARAH BIGGS

Talking About Anorexia
How to cope with life without starving
MAROUSHKA MONRO

Talking About Miscarriage
SARAH MURPHY

Ten Steps to Positive Living
DR WINDY DRYDEN

Think Your Way to Happiness
DR WINDY DRYDEN AND JACK GORDON

Understanding Obsessions and Compulsions
A self-help manual
DR FRANK TALLIS

Understanding Your Personality
Myers-Briggs and more
PATRICIA HEDGES

A Weight Off Your Mind
How to stop worrying about your body size
SUE DYSON

When your Child Comes Out
ANNE LOVELL

You and Your Varicose Veins
DR PATRICIA GILBERT

Overcoming Common Problems

TALKING ABOUT ANOREXIA

Maroushka Monro

First published in Great Britain in 1992
Sheldon Press, SPCK, Marylebone Road, London NW1 4DU

Revised and updated twice 1996

British Library Cataloguing in Publication Data
A catalogue record for this book is available from the British Library
ISBN 0–85969–751–7

Photoset by Deltatype Ltd, Ellesmere Port, Cheshire
Printed in Great Britain by Biddles Ltd, Guildford and King's Lynn

Contents

Acknowledgements

My acknowledgements and thanks are due to:

All the *Just Seventeen* readers who wrote to me about their experience of anorexia – and those whose accounts and poems I've been able to include in this book; Christine Halek, Clinical Nurse Specialist, St George's Hospital; Eating Disorders Association; Anorexia and Bulimia Care; Royal College of Psychiatry; Joanna Moriarty at Sheldon Press for her encouragement and support; Freida Greene.

NOTE: *All names included in the text and case histories have been changed, but they are real accounts of girls' experiences.*

The key to your happiness and contentment lies
deep within each one of you,
within your own hearts and minds . . .

Eileen Caddy, 'The Key to Happiness is Within',
in William Bloom (ed.), *The New Age.*

Foreword

Maroushka Monro, herself a recovered anorexic, has written a sensitive and insightful book on anorexia, which should be a rewarding read for all concerned with the problem.

Highly readable, the book is written in a straightforward style and addresses the reader directly and sympathetically. Maroushka Monro talks as a caring and understanding friend, and examines the difficulties and pressures that contribute to a young person becoming anorexic.

The book is divided into three parts. Part One explains the anorexic's rationale of 'why diet?' It examines the pressures on young girls today to be attractive and the 'ideal' shape and size, from the endless images of slim super-models to the barrage of TV and magazine commercials. It questions whether this uniformity is healthy and how the quest for the 'perfect' body becomes obsessive, to the exclusion of all other interests and activities. The differences between slimming and anorexia are defined and the health risks stated in no uncertain terms.

Part Two looks at the importance of recognising that there is a problem and how to ask for help. Maroushka Monro emphasises this process of recognition as the first, most important step to recovery. A very helpful section at the end of the book lists organisations and help-line numbers which give support.

Part Three looks at ways of coping with life's difficulties without resorting to starving oneself. Maroushka Monro draws upon her experience as agony aunt on *Just Seventeen* magazine to explore the wide range of difficulties young people encounter growing up.

The Eating Disorders Association strongly recommends this excellent book, which provides both insights and practical advice on how to cope with anorexia.

Anne Moore
EDA
1996

Introduction

In the three years I spent as *Just Seventeen* magazine's advice columnist, the question I was asked most often was, 'Are the letters *real* . . . or do you make them up?'! Firstly, I can't imagine anyone having the imagination and the energy to invent so many letters each week. But, the answer is a definite '*No*', for the simple reason that I didn't need to make them up. Each week I received literally hundreds of letters from young people asking for help or advice. It would obviously have been a happier situation if these leters weren't in fact real, because that would have meant fewer young people were experiencing problems of one kind of another. But the fact remains that many people obviously felt the need to share their worries and thoughts and it seems to me far better to do this than bottle things up and try to cope alone.

Many young people have written to me about relationships, boyfriends . . . families . . . best friends. The questions 'How do I attract the attention of the boy I fancy?' and 'Should I say yes to having sex?' are the two most common problems. There's rarely the same answer for everyone, because each situation varies, as do individuals. Lots of people have written about shyness, jealousy, depression and the way they look. A lack of self-confidence is something which has cropped up often in your letters. Then there's the question of loneliness – frequently you mention the lack of friendships due to shyness. So, in a way, one problem causes you yet another difficulty to cope with.

Quite a number of people have written to me because they have been sexually abused. When girls have related these experiences to me, I've always been touched by the sense of guilt these letters invariably convey. I realize you often feel it's somehow your fault if something like this has happened to you and you need reassurance and support in order to overcome these feelings.

Many of you have asked specific questions about periods, health problems and contraception. Worries about relationships inevitably include your feelings about sex. Both emotionally and physically the start of a sexual relationship can bring up a whole lot of different problems you feel you just can't resolve alone. Why should you have to when everything is so unknown and new, and in many ways unsettling?

What's all this got to do with anorexia?

Amongst all these different kinds of letters have also been the ones from many of you who are preoccupied with your weight and dieting. The words 'I think I may be anorexic' are familiar ones. Sometimes I've been told it's a friend who's hardly eating a thing and is getting 'much too thin'.

These letters concern me, because I sense they speak for many of the other kinds of problems I've mentioned previously. This is because anorexia is a cry for help which isn't just about food, eating and your weight. And just as worrying are the letters which have told me that all your anger and difficult emotions get directed back at yourself, so that you try to harm yourself in some other way. I very much wanted to write this book for you, because you are concerned about anorexia – and other things besides.

I don't want to mislead you into thinking I can come up with the 'magic answer' to all your problems, or tell you exactly why you as an individual have become anorexic. My aim is to help you look a little closer at what's happening and why, so that you can try to get a different perspective on things and find the right kind of help and support. The second part of the book looks at accepting something is wrong, and taking action; learning how to make progress and cope with setbacks. I've also included three girls' accounts of what happened to them. In the third part of the book we'll look more closely at some of the problems many people have written about, to see how to find ways of resolving them without starving yourself as a 'punishment'.

Perhaps just as importantly I write from my own experience of anorexia. So I believe I can understand, to some extent, what you are going through. I don't think I can give you one single reason why I began to starve myself. It was really a combination of a whole lot of things, though at the time I wasn't at all aware of what was happening. Strangely enough, though, I can remember exactly *when* it started more or less to the minute. It was as if a small voice in my head started telling me I had to stop eating, even though I wasn't – and never had been – in the least bit overweight. It never occurred to me that this was to be the beginning of a long difficult fight between me and food. It just felt as though something very powerful was happening to me. After I had lost the first few pounds, I started to feel really good, with a huge sense of achievement. I also experienced something I had never felt before – the *belief* that I was in control of my life for the first time. I also felt incredibly isolated, almost as though I was living on a different planet to everyone else!

It took a long while for me to recognize, acknowledge and openly admit that something was terribly wrong. I think the turning point for me was the realization that food – or rather lack of it – was controlling my thoughts, my whole life, rather than *me* being in control as I'd previously thought. I desperately wanted things to change.

Asking for help wasn't easy, but I can assure you it was a tremendous relief when I stopped pretending to myself that I could manage, while continuing to live my life in such a limited and self-destructive way. I found help and support – and gradually met others who shared my problem. I went to groups in which people really understood my experience. I began to realize that not eating had been my way of blocking out so many difficult feelings and needs until eventually I didn't even know what they were. Talking about the problems helped me to feel less isolated and gave me much-needed support. I also began to realize that recovering from anorexia meant letting go of a lot of one-track thinking about myself and food. Most importantly, I *wanted* to be free of anorexia . . . I really wanted things to be different.

Unlike the onset of my anorexia, I can't say there was an exact moment when I suddenly felt better. I didn't wake up one morning knowing I was 'cured'. Anorexia is not like that. It's a gradual process, involving getting in touch with all kinds of feelings, learning to value yourself, letting go of your old behaviour . . . learning to grow and wanting to change.

When you're caught up in something as strong and powerful

as anorexia, I realize that it's hard to imagine ever being able to change. I think the poem at the beginning of Chapter 1 says a lot about how many of you think. I would be very surprised if many of you couldn't identify with it! All too often you have described yourselves as 'gross', 'a fat lump', or just downright 'revolting', which is a sad, and I'm sure unfair, reflection of how you really are.

Personally, I feel that unless you've had some kind of experience of anorexia, it can often be very hard indeed to understand what it's like to suffer from this condition. If you are anorexic, you could well have very mixed feelings about wanting to get better. I can't pretend to you that these feelings will just disappear overnight. They won't! In some ways, it is far easier to push things to the back of your mind and get on with concentrating on all that calorie counting and over-exercising. *Pretending* you've already eaten your tea with your best mate may seem the easier option to actually doing it.

I can remember my dad once 'bribing' me to eat by offering me £1 for every pound of weight I'd agree to put on. I decided against getting rich, because losing weight seemed more important to me at the time. This shows just how unreasonable you can become when you are anorexic! It is also just one sad example of how desperate other people can become to help you – and how extremely difficult it is for them to break through the barriers you put up to resist that help.

The fear of 'letting go' of anorexia, and the need to be free of the compulsion to lose more and more weight, seem to fight with each other. You probably think you'll be struggling with it for ever, but, I can assure you, there *is* a way out.

One thing is certain, this isn't a battle you need fight all on your own. I remember thinking at the time that nobody could possibly understand what I was going through. It was a bit like being shut away in a room on your own, completely out of reach. In many ways you *are*, until you can acknowledge and face up to the fact that something is wrong and you simply can't manage alone.

I know from all the letters I've received that anorexia can even hold a kind of fascination for you. It's true that you sometimes also fear it, yet at the same time you can't often imagine alternatives to the dieting and weighing seven stone 'ideal'. Growing up can, and and should be, an exciting and pleasurable experience. But, it can also feel as though you're the only one who's confused about it. I hope I've so far managed to reassure you that this is far from the case.

Above all, the letters which have made me realize just how much more you need to understand about your weight, dieting and your thoughts about food, are those which tell me time and again that 'I wish I could become anorexic, in order to be slim . . .'.

My hope is that reading this book will at least help you to see things differently.

PART ONE

About Anorexia

FAT

(*a poem by Sandra James, aged 17*)

I wish I was thinner.
Really much slimmer,
than a great big lump.
I wish I could diet,
I really must try it.
All this weight I'll try to dump.
My legs are fat,
my stomach is too,
I don't really know what to do.
Cut out the biscuits,
cut out the chips,
to trim a few inches
off my hips.
My thighs are a mess
and I really detest,
the shape that I'm in.
Oh what I'd give,
if only to live,
like a model, really slim.

From Sandra James, *Teenage Years*
(Reproduced by kind permission of Fine Publishing, Priory Lane, Toft Monks, Beccles, Suffolk NR34 0EZ)

1

What is Anorexia Nervosa

Anorexia nervosa is often described as 'the slimmer's disease'. So I think a good way to start explaining about it is to tell you that anorexia *isn't* just a case of over-dieting and slimming. A lot of people go on slimming diets without going on to become anorexic.

'Anorexic' is a medical term which means literally 'loss of appetite'. 'Nervosa' very simply means nervous. But if you suffer from this condition, you will probably be feeling confused by this misleading name. The fact is that far from losing your appetite you will undoubtedly feel hungry much of the time. This hunger is so successfully pushed away that you wouldn't dream of admitting it – not to others, not even to yourself. Some doctors refer to people with anorexia as 'anorectic', but it means the same and throughout this book I'll use the words anorexia and anorexic.

To understand anorexia nervosa, you first need to realize that you are denying yourself food as a way of controlling your life, not just because you want to lose a bit of weight for your best mate's party. The whole point about starving yourself is that it seems to give you a way of not having to confront anger, fears and problems which may seem so huge and complicated that you can't even say for sure what they are, let alone face and overcome them. You may also feel that by denying yourself food you somehow set yourself apart from other people, and this makes you feel 'good' – maybe even special. I can remember thinking how out of control *other* people must be – and how greedy, just because they were eating normally. It didn't enter my head that I was actually addicted to *not* eating and it was me, not others, who had a problem!

How can you tell if you are anorexic?

There are a number of signs. I'm not suggesting you should decide you are definitely anorexic just because one or two things apply to you. But I think if you are reading this book, you will already be sufficiently worried or preoccupied with your weight and food at least to suspect that something is wrong. (In Part Two, I will explain how to go about seeking help because I know from experience that taking the first step towards finding help is often the hardest.)

Let's look at some of the warning signs, which should alert you that eating isn't the happy, pleasant, life-giving and fun pastime it should be.

- Do you have a strong fear of weighing over seven stone?
- Have you lost a lot of weight but look in the mirror and think you are enormous and lumpy, even though you are underweight and family/friends tell you you're too thin?
- Do you strictly limit the amount you eat, perhaps counting calories, or weighing things, so you don't 'overdo' it?
- Do you secretly exercise as much as possible, even when you're too tired, or unwell, in an attempt to burn off calories and lose more weight?
- Do you constantly think about food and how much you're 'allowed' to eat?
- Do you make yourself sick, or take laxatives, to 'get rid' of food?
- Do you weigh yourself once, or even more often, every day?
- Do you love reading recipes and giving other people food, which you don't share?
- Do you skip meals and pretend to your family that you've already eaten?
- Do you panic if you can't eat exactly what you've planned – say a tiny amount of cottage cheese and an apple?
- Do you write down the amounts you've eaten in a note pad/diary, keeping a close check on every mouthful?
- Do you feel isolated, unhappy and irritable, yet unable to confide in anyone?
- Do you feel that denying yourself food is all you've got to hold onto?
- *Have your periods stopped?*

There's a fair chance that if some, or all, of these things apply to you, then eating normally has become a problem, though you may still deny that anything is actually wrong. After all, you're coping and proving that you're able to do at least one thing very well indeed – starve yourself. Maybe you feel quite superior about it, perhaps sharing the view I once had that other people eat just because they're out of control and basically greedy.

Denying yourself food may, in fact, seem to give you a sense of being 'someone' and provide you with a feeling of identity. You may even desperately want to get better, to be able to eat properly again, but you don't want to put on weight in the process. I can honestly identify with that wish because when I was anorexic I would have given anything to be able to eat my favourite foods without worrying or being afraid of what might 'happen'. But I just couldn't risk going above the totally unrealistic low weight I had decided to stick to. I think I truly believed that if I ate even a mouthful more than my daily 'allowance', something really terrible would happen to me, almost like a punishment. Does that ring any bells with you?

It can feel as though you're being 'good' when you are starving yourself. But, in fact, if you become anorexic you are actually being extremely 'bad' and cruel to yourself, treating your body with the lack of love and respect which both you and it deserve.

Anorexia is not an illness like chicken pox or measles which people catch from one another, or 'happen' to get. It's a self-destructive way of trying to cope with difficult feelings, needs and problems – a way of trying to gain control in your life. If you can acknowledge this, you will begin to see what's really going on.

I remember once receiving a letter from a particular reader – Karen – who had convinced herself that because her friend Julie was anorexic, she too was likely to become a sufferer of this condition. She wrote:

> Julie only *pretends* to eat during the day at school, but she either gives her sandwiches away or throws them in the bin. She's made me promise not to tell her mum, but I really hate lying for her. The trouble is, when I see that she's not eating, I wonder if the same thing will happen to me and I'm really scared about it . . .

When you are totally preoccupied with thoughts about food,

diets, exercise, your weight – and losing even more weight – you have little time or energy to think of anything else. You can't even decide clearly about day-to-day problems such as which colour jumper to choose, let alone be able to give some thought to the problems you've never been able to deal with. Decision making becomes one extra problem, because you've learnt to shut things off to such an extent that choices of any kind seem to throw you completely. Not eating is the anorexic way of 'putting off' thinking about anything else. One thing's for sure. Your problems aren't instantly resolved just because you've become thinner. Hidden away, maybe . . . but that's not the same thing at all.

I remember an incident which occurred when I was involved in running a self-help group for young women with eating disorders. At the time I was still recovering from anorexia myself and had lots of my own problems to share with the others. Basically, this was the whole idea of the group – to give mutual support. Some of the girls were quite large and were compulsive eaters who believed that their only problem in life was being overweight. One girl in particular was very unfriendly and hostile towards me. I just couldn't understand what, if anything, I'd done to upset her. Eventually, through talking in the group, she confessed that she felt I had 'no business to be in the group', since I was thin and therefore couldn't possibly have any problems! I soon put her right about that and the group continued without the bad feeling between us.

I can assure you that if you suffer from anorexia, you are by no means alone. The Royal College of Psychiatry have estimated that there are 10,000 secondary school girls in the UK with anorexia and that 1 in 500 girls between the ages of 15 and 25 suffer from this condition. It is also estimated that 25 per cent of sufferers are young males – and the numbers are believed to be growing. About a hundred young people die from anorexia each year. You may not think this is a very high number, but remember we're talking about a *young* normally healthy age-group in which 100 deaths of people under 25 is a significant number.

Becoming anorexic puts everything 'on hold', but doesn't

resolve anything. It endangers your health, your happiness, your sense of freedom . . . your life. It is far more rewarding, courageous and true to yourself to try confronting your feelings – your need to be accepted and loved – and to recognize your value. Both to yourself and to others.

Once you've found a way of coping through being anorexic, why on earth should you let go of it? Being anorexic means that you have developed a way of living – a liftstyle – which seems to make everything possible. For instance, you may imagine yourself becoming much prettier, more likeable and generally more acceptable, if only you can lose just a few more pounds . . . and a few more . . . and a few more. In other words it seems that if you can control what you eat, you can control everything about yourself and what happens to you.

The problem is that lots of things we *want* to happen aren't altogether realistic or possible, and whether or not you starve yourself and keep your weight at a dangerously low level won't actually change that reality! Accepting what is – and isn't – possible in your life, and then setting about doing something *constructive* to achieve what you want, will leave you feeling less powerless and, in the long run, in far *more* control than not eating will ever allow you to be.

Anorexia is a way of not even looking at what is possible, and a way of pushing aside everything which hurts or requires you to admit you have choices. Being anorexic means that you have found a way of not acknowledging you have any needs beyond losing weight.

I think you know in your heart that everyone has at least *some* needs and you have probably got lots! This isn't an admission of weakness. Having needs doesn't mean you are bad or greedy or unloveable. Turn it around the other way and see that pretending you have absolutely no needs doesn't mean you are good either.

Starving yourself is dangerous. It's as simple as that, yet it seems anything but simple when all you can think about is whether or not you should have had one or two bites of that apple. Anorexia becomes such a habit that you may see any other way of living from day to day as just too scary to even think about. The very nature of the condition means that you may find it hard to accept that there *are* other ways of coping.

I hope this chapter has given you a better understanding of what it actually means to be anorexic. I think this is an important step, because if you tend to look upon it as just a slimming diet which has got out of hand, you may even believe it's somehow desirable – even glamorous – to become anorexic. I can assure you, nothing could be further from the truth.

There is nothing even remotely glamorous about anorexia.

People who go on hunger strikes as a protest are often seen as heroic and brave. OK, anorexia is a kind of hunger strike. But, the huge difference is this: you are striking against *yourself.* If you suffer from anorexia, you are basically saying a very loud 'No' to everything you need. With every one more needless pound you lose, you are agreeing to give yourself a very hard time. Understanding this is one of the first steps towards facing up to what it means to become anorexic.

Finally, I want to mention that boys, too, can become anorexic. I have to admit that I've only once received a letter from a boy who is worried about it, but this doesn't necessarily mean that none of the boys who read *Just Seventeen*'s advice column are sufferers. It may have much more to do with a reluctance to talk about it.

When I consider how difficult it is for many female anorexics to seek help, even though we are generally far more used to talking about our problems, it's not really surprising that a male anorexic may be very slow in coming forward. On the other hand, boys write about *other* problems apart from anorexia, which I think goes to show that they share similar worries.

Boys are generally encouraged to be 'strong' and showing emotions doesn't always come as second nature when a macho image is seen as 'cool'. Gazza went a long way towards proving that tears aren't the sign of a wimp, just someone who's prepared openly to show their feelings – male or female. Also, boys tend to worry less than girls about being fat, although bullying because of being overweight can certainly create the same pressures and problems for boys. And sometimes this results in anorexia. So, although this book may primarily concern girls, it certainly doesn't exclude boys. If you are a boy suffering from anorexia, I hope you will find something in this book with which you can identify.

2

Why diet?

Gazing at her mirror image
she sees, not a reflection,
but a cruel deception . . .

These few lines are part of a poem I wrote when I was recovering from anorexia. I wanted to include them here, because one important thing always seemed to crop up in many people's letters about dieting. You often see yourselves as fat, but if you enclose a photo, or even just describe your weight and height, it is pretty obvious that you aren't in the least bit overweight. You are looking in the mirror as I once did and seeing something quite different from your real reflection.

Thin is beautiful . . . or is it?

Look around you and you will see absolutely loads of images of what our society has decided is the 'ideal' shape and size for women. You'll soon get the message if you look at various fashion pictures, or watch a few TV commercials. We get bombarded by so-called 'miracle diets' and 'exercise plans' which are designed to mould us into what's actually a very artificial thinness. But think about this very carefully. *Can it really make sense that we should all have a uniform look, size and shape?*

Each and every one of us is different . . . so why on earth should someone with a large-ish frame try to force themselves to 'shape up' into something which just isn't natural or healthy for them?

Another point to bear in mind is that both television and photographs are well known for making people look larger than they really are. Photographic models, for example, are often asked to slim in order to counter-balance this slight distortion. Does that mean that all young girls and women have to go on a diet so they can look like a model? That would be like saying we all have to go for breathing lessons, just because professional singers do so to enhance their voices!

Lots of girls who have written to me don't get on that well with food. That sounds a bit strange, I know. After all, you probably don't think of food as something you have any kind of relationship with, do you? Many of you have a huge amount of guilt associated with food, even though lots of girls secretly absolutely adore eating. How much is too much? What should I eat? Is it 'good' or 'bad'? Should I admit I've eaten it? Do any of those questions sound familiar?

You no doubt think that if you don't eat too much you are doing the 'right' thing. But if you go for the Mars Bar you've been 'naughty'. One of my pet hates was the 'naughty but nice' TV cream cake ad., which to me just emphasizes that sense of guilt most of us (usually female) are supposed to feel about indulging ourselves. On the other hand, that macho trucker with his Yorkie Bar was seen as a healthy lad, with an appetite to match!

It's a joke, isn't it? The fact is, until you stop seeing food as public enemy number one, you will quite literally always be in a battle with it.

During adolescence, it is only natural to go through a time of self consciousness, lack of self-confidence and a lot of uncertainty – about yourselves, what you want to be, the future, who you are . . . generally 'what's it all about?' It's clear by the ways in which you've described yourselves that you feel how you look on the outside will somehow improve what's going on inside. But, really, it's the other way round. No amount of slimness, lack of spots or greasy hair will make up for lack of love for the person you are – in other words, acceptance of yourself.

Don't get me wrong, I'm not for one minute suggesting that to look good is a waste of time. Far from it. Making the best of your appearance is a great boost and will certainly give you extra confidence. *But*, trying to re-shape your body, or be extra slim, won't make you happy if you are sad about the break up of a relationship, angry about a past experience which hurt you, or lacking friendships. There are ways of resolving these problems without counting calories and starving yourself.

Is food a really 'big deal' in your family?

Let's face it, eating is an important part of our lives with other people. If you accept food it gives pleasure to the person who has provided it. On the other hand, refusing it can sometimes offend that person, especially if it's your mum or family members. Perhaps you can see that saying 'No' to food could sometimes be your way of expressing your feelings – of anger, resentment, even sadness. All families have arguments, that's perfectly normal. It's easy to think of food and arguments in the same light, if say, all family disagreements seem to go on around the tea-table. Pushing your plate away, or saying 'I'm not hungry' when in actual fact you're ravenous, could *really* mean 'I'm upset', 'I'm hurt', 'I'm furious'.

Expressing these actual feelings – with any luck away from the tea-table – would help you feel a whole lot better than denying yourself food. For instance, if someone has upset you at home, or you feel angry about a situation you think is unfair, try to discuss it with the particular member of your family concerned. It's no use telling someone else and avoiding a confrontation with the person who's upset you, because this is likely to leave you with unresolved and difficult feelings. Instead, say to whoever it is something like, 'What you said to me earlier really upset me and I felt awful for the rest of the day . . .' This gives the other person a clear idea of your reaction and then you can both talk about it and try to sort out what happened between you. Try not to be accusing; on the other hand, if you feel angry try to make this clear. That way you are likely to feel much better and won't harbour resentment. Also, the other person won't receive 'mixed messages' from you – such as a refusal of food at the dinner table.

Perhaps you also feel you may be more acceptable to one or both of your parents if only you could lose some of that 'unattractive bulk'? Even if this *were* true (and it rarely is), why on earth should you want to diet for someone else – whether it is family, friend, or boyfriend? Please think about your reason for wanting to lose weight, even if you know you aren't anorexic. Are you doing it to please yourself, or because someone has asked you to . . . even threatened you? I was always outraged when I received a letter saying, 'I fancy this boy at school, but he says he won't go out with me because I'm too fat.' Or, 'He'll only go out with me if I go on a diet.' What a nerve! If someone doesn't like and accept you for what you are *now*, then for goodness sake let them go.

Some of you seem to go on diets because a so-called friend has called you something like 'piggy' or 'fatso', or pointed out that you eat more than their six-foot-tall brother. Perhaps an elderly relative may have commented on how 'well' you look, just as you're tucking into your second plate of chips. So you may decide then and there to diet. Why? Did it occur to you that you should *before* these remarks were made? And why, in any case, should you take everything other people say so literally and seriously? Not everyone is totally honest – and not everyone has your best interests at heart when they make these comments. Try to make some of your own judgements about yourself, instead of putting your entire well-being in the hands of a creep who goes round calling people silly names! If you can learn to laugh these things off more and become really and truly in touch with how you look and feel, believe me, you won't allow chance comments like that to throw you into a fit of despair about what is more often than not *imaginary* 'fat'.

Then there are sponsored diets

While I wholeheartedly support charities which raise money for deserving causes, I would like to discourage you from supporting these causes by going on a sponsored diet. There are so many other ways in which you can help raise money for charities: all you have to do is write to them for alternative ideas to dieting. I'm dead against any young person going on a strict diet unless she (or he) is advised by a doctor that it is necessary for health or medical reasons. Even then, no reputable doctor is likely to put a young person on a 'crash' diet. Crash dieting – losing a fair amount of weight in a short space of time – is unhealthy and usually totally ineffective in the long term. OK, so you may jump on the scales and find you weigh less, but most of it will be replaced in double quick time as soon as you start to eat properly again. Also, when you go on an *unsupervised* diet, in an attempt to lose weight fast, you confuse your body into thinking it is 'starving', and your metabolic rate slows down to make up for the reduced intake of food. If you repeatedly go on crash diets your body will find it very difficult to adjust, especially if you alternate periods of dieting with over-eating. That's why the majority of people who tell you they are always on a diet fail to lose weight.

If you count the calories every day, of every mouthful of food you eat, whether it's for a sponsored diet or one you've put yourself on, it's bound to make you feel restricted, bored and obsessed with what you're eating. That's bad news, because once again it takes the fun out of what should be a pleasure – eating. Going on a weight-reducing diet of any kind which hasn't been recommended by a doctor is one way in which many people begin to use food, or the lack of it, to cover up things which are really bothering them and can lead to over-dieting . . . and anorexia. Remember, anorexia isn't something you can 'get' for a week and then easily shake off. It can take months, even years, to recover.

I've written this chapter about slimming because I think it's important for you to be able to recognize the difference between what I'll call 'ordinary slimming' and becoming anorexic. Lots of people go on diets, but only a few of them will become anorexic. The majority of people who diet for the sake of it find it a huge bore, get fed up with the whole thing after a few days, and then just carry on as before. Someone who becomes anorexic won't necessarily have been overweight – as I wasn't. If you're unsure about your weight, check with your GP.

There's a big difference, then, between ordinary slimming and starving yourself. Going on an unsupervised diet puts you at risk of becoming too caught up in losing weight and can get out of hand. The only way to maintain a healthy weight, one which is right for *you* and takes in account your age, height, build, even family traits, is to maintain a balanced, nutritious and varied diet, combined with a sensible amount of exercise you enjoy doing. (I'll say more about this later on in the book.) This doesn't mean slavishly following recipes, spending lots of money, or boring yourself to tears by chomping on carrots and avoiding chocs and biscuits for the rest of your life!

During my recovery I met someone called Susie Orbach, a well-known therapist and author. She helped to change my whole way of thinking about diets – and food. I met her around the time she opened The Women's Therapy Centre in London. I went to several of the groups at the Centre before running my own, but I was absolutely staggered at her suggestions. She sat there and told us that we should go away and eat *anything* we liked – nothing, but nothing was forbidden. After years of all of us in the group believing that 'nice' really did mean 'naughty', we found her suggestions literally 'hard to swallow'! One thing she said has always stayed in my mind, and you too may find it worth thinking about. If you're about to eat a meal which you don't really fancy just to get to the pudding, why not just go for the pudding? There's no law which says you've got to eat things in any particular order, or 'suffer' before you can have what you really want.

It took me a while before I could accept this, but once I did . . . I've never looked back! Try to think of food as being something pleasurable – more importantly, something you deserve. Food can often be a great comfort, too, especially sweet things. While I'm in no way suggesting you start living off a diet of chocs. and cakes which wouldn't do a lot for your general health, I am saying that if you don't think of certain foods as being 'wicked', you'll feel much happier and relaxed about eating. You may find it hard to believe, but you are far more likely to maintain your correct weight if you eat some of all the things you like included in a nourishing diet, than if you diet all the time.

As a recovered anorexic, I find it very disheartening to listen to girls discussing their diets and what they should and shouldn't eat, especially when there is no one around who's in the slightest bit overweight. I've spent whole lunch hours within ear-shot of talk which goes something like: 'I've had one tuna fish sandwich and an apple, so I'm *allowed* to have so many calories tonight.' Or, 'If I only eat some of this now, I can have some tea tonight . . .' I look over and see a group of very slim girls, and my heart sinks.

So, again – try hard to think about the reasons *why* you feel the need to lose weight. If you are honestly worried about your size, you should always go to your doctor and talk it over with him/

her. I know that many of you hate going to your doctor, because you feel embarrassed or stupid. I can understand how you feel, but it's worth trying hard to overcome this reluctance. You can be sure that your doctor has seen hundreds of other young people with similar problems to your own and is not going to think you are wasting his/her time. If your doctor genuinely feels it is in your best interest to change or adjust your diet, he/she will say so and advise you, or will possibly refer you to someone else who can help.

If you are anorexic and have been cutting down the amount of food you eat and what you eat, there's no way you will want someone to tell you how much you should weight. You've no doubt decided yourself that you want to be a certain weight and nobody's going to convince you otherwise. You may have already reached that 'ideal' weight and then decided you just need to lose a bit more. In Chapter 4, 'Jane's story', you will see how Jane thought she had everything under control. She'd set herself a goal – six and a half stone – and really believed she'd be able to stop when she reached this weight. But this wasn't at all the case because by then things had already gone too far for her to give up her 'hunger strike' without help. This isn't slimming to be healthy and fit, this is your 'hunger strike' . . . your protest against caring for yourself. See the difference and you will find it that much harder to confuse the business of slimming with anorexia nervosa.

3

What happens when you starve yourself?

You may be thinking this is a daft question. After all, you can easily answer it yourself . . . you get thin, of course! You're right. But, I feel it's also important for you to realize that becoming anorexic isn't just a short-cut to slimness, with no other consequences. In no way is it an attractive state – either physically or emotionally. Being at a healthy weight which suits you as an individual will also mean that you have good skin, bright eyes, good circulation, energy, regular periods, healthy nails and hair, to name but a few of the things we tend to take for granted when we are looking after ourselves properly. Anorexia robs you of these things and doesn't even give you a pleasant-to-look-at healthy slimness. It gives you bony *thinness* which, amusing though it may sound, can actually *hurt* when you sit down. Although, obviously, the main symptom of not eating enough is that you will lose weight, there are other signs you may well experience as your weight drops. Personally, I wasn't prepared for these side-effects; I had no idea what was going to happen to me. After all, I thought I was in control, so what was happening?

I want you to be aware of these possible symptoms, because these signs can serve as a warning that things have gone much too far. Also, they are unpleasant side-effects of a condition which you may still, deep down, see as OK – even desirable.

If you are anorexic you will undoubtedly be terrified of getting fat and you will be totally preoccupied with your weight and what does, or more to the point what *doesn't*, go into your mouth. Your whole life will revolve around this issue, and so one of the symptoms besides losing weight will be this obsession which can lead to that feeling of isolation I talked about earlier. You may also become very secretive and deceitful, even if you are by nature a very open and honest person. Because your main concern is to avoid eating, you think nothing of making up all kinds of stories about, for example, meals you've 'eaten', or 'headaches' which prevent you from sitting down with other people for a meal. From my own experience, these lies can make you feel even more alone. They separate you from the people you want so much to be close to and make it seem even more difficult to receive the love you may desperately want. After all, most people know when you're making these things up and quite understandably they sometimes react in a negative way to your stories.

From a purely physical point of view if you are female your periods will stop and you will experience a feeling of restlessness. This isn't the same as having the kind of energy which goes hand-in-hand with good health and being 'fuelled' with the right amount of food. This restlessness happens when you are hungry and cannot stay still. A bit like an animal on the prowl! It is not what I would call a 'happy energy'. You may wake up in the early hours of the morning, unable to sleep any longer. Maybe you will even start to exercise, feeling that if you can get in some press-ups before dawn, you will work away yet another few pounds . . . some more calories.

Many anorexics suffer from severe constipation, abdominal pains, dizzy spells and swollen stomachs, faces and ankles. You may possibly also notice a growth of downy hair on your body while, on the other hand, the hair on your head may become dry, brittle and thinner than before. You may also develop a slow pulse rate, which in simple terms means that your heart isn't working properly, because it lacks the calories it needs to keep it going in the way it should. Weight loss can also affect your reproductive development, because of changes in your hormones. Bad circulation will mean that your skin may become cold and dry, possibly even discoloured.

You may think that becoming restless, for instance, is no big deal – in fact, this kind of need for activity may be something you use as a kind of defense against other people's comments about your condition. 'There's no need to worry – I'm full of energy . . . I don't get tired' was one of my favourite ways of answering back to yet another show of concern from someone. However, I can assure you this situation changes, because your body can only take so much abuse. You simply cannot go on starving yourself without becoming weak and easily tired.

These symptoms are unpleasant to think about. They are even more unpleasant to experience. If I were to spare you the reality of what can happen to you, I don't feel I would be doing you much of a favour. Also, I tend to think it may help you to realize that all these symptoms *will* go away given time and gradual recovery. You are not being punished for being anorexic, as some people seem to imagine. Your body is reacting to the way it is being treated – by *you*. You are punishing yourself when what you really need is love, understanding and help.

One thing I know will be hard for you as a sufferer to realize is that the less you eat the harder it will become for you to see things as they really are. Not only will you look in the mirror and see 'large' or 'fat' where there is none, but, as I said about myself in the beginning of the book, you will probably think everyone else is out of line – not *you*. People who are close to you may well feel frustrated – even angry – by your refusal to admit anything's wrong. Saying 'I'm fine' when it is pretty obvious that you're anything but, can be a challenge for even the best of your friends or adoring family.

Believe me, deep inside you there's a need to be helped – you may even wish someone would take over completely and look after you. It's hard to admit this because you probably fear that you're not really worth it. You may also think that getting help just means forcing you to eat and put on weight, and *no way* will you agree to that. Perhaps you imagine that the only thing you're really good at is not eating? But, you've no doubt already discovered that it's not quite a simple as that, because that feeling of control is sometimes taken over by a sense of being trapped – which is confusing to say the least. Try to get in touch with the part of yourself which knows you cannot cope alone and wants to find a new way of being happy. This is a true sign of wanting to take control of your life without hurting yourself. It's the positive way.

Some people abuse alcohol or drugs as a way of coping with their problems and they deserve to seek help. Anorexia is a way of abusing food. You, too, deserve to seek out and receive support. If you suffer from anorexia, you may as I once did, believe that if you start to think about anything else and actually begin to feel what is really happening, this new understanding will be more difficult to cope with than the condition itself. Possibly, you will imagine that the symptoms I have talked about are more tolerable than 'letting go' of starving yourself.

I'm not going to tell you that understanding your needs is necessarily going to be straightforward – or an overnight revelation. After all, you've become expert at hiding your feelings and needs, so it stands to reason that finding them will be a gradual process. There's a saying which goes 'ignorance is bliss', but no way can this ever refer to anorexia. Not knowing what you want and turning your back on yourself by starving yourself is a very high price to pay. In a sense, time stands still while you are anorexic. You may believe that you don't have the power to change what's happening. But you *do* have the power to choose between staying 'safe' with anorexia and taking responsibilities for your life by finding a new way of coping. Moving forward may seem a frightening prospect – but it's a far happier place to be than with the suffering of anorexia.

4

Jane's story

It's really hard to say how it started. A year before I made the decision to lose weight I started exercising really secretly. It was my image to be very slim, but I didn't want anyone to know about all the effort I was putting into it. I didn't think I was slim at the time – I thought I was too big. Then, that Easter, we went away for a few days and I remember drinking hot chocolate all the time, thinking 'This is *it* . . . From now on I'm going to stop doing all that and I'm going to diet.' So, chocolate was my last treat before it all began. But I kept it really secret, though my dad realized quite soon that something was wrong. He had to go away for a week and when he came back he noticed the difference in me, even in just one week.

I used to write all these charts out and weighed myself every single day. I knew exactly how much I was going to eat and weighed everything. From Easter to the summer holidays I was just completely lost. My one aim was to be six and a half stone – God knows why – and nothing else mattered.

What seemed to trigger things off for me was a friendship. I'd been best friends with this girl for years.

We were friends with a group of other people but I didn't really want to be as I always felt I was just tagging along, and that I wasn't particularly special. My best friend became more and more friendly with another girl and she seemed to absolutely worship her. In a way I just wanted to get out of the situation and I thought, 'Great, she's got a new friend'. But she wouldn't let me go and they both seemed to keep inviting me along to things. I always felt as if it was just tagging along, not joining in properly. I was there, but they seemed to ignore me a lot of the time. And that was about the time when I stopped eating.

I'd read quite a bit about anorexia, but it seemed to me then that it was only if you were stupid and careless and let it get out of control there'd be a problem. It's *much* worse than that though. I remember at the time, my mum started talking to my sister about the dangers of anorexia, but it was *me*, not her, who wasn't eating!

I'd decided that I was going to get down to six-and-a-half stone and, then, after that I'd stop and be fine! I thought it was dead easy. I thought I was completely in control of it. I thought – well – people can call it anorexia, but it isn't really because I'm in control. Then, it got to the summer and my weight carried on going down. I just didn't want to eat, even though I'd reached the 'target' weight, I didn't want to consume calories. I'd look at an ice cream and just see layers of fat.

In a way, I wanted to go just a bit below six-and-a-half stone, because then I felt it would be OK to eat – I'd be allowed to in a way, I'd be giving myself some leeway, I'd weigh myself every morning and if my weight had gone up I'd just freak. I remember thinking for ages, all this is never going to go away. I kept telling my mum and dad it's OK because I know what I'm doing. I kept saying yes I *do* eat . . . of course I do! Some days I wouldn't eat anything at all but I'd tell my parents I'd eaten at school, or with my friends somewhere. Or, I tried to convince them that I was just missing one meal a day, when really I hadn't eaten anything.

All the people in the group I used to hang around with were lighter than me and I loathed them so much. I used always to think that my mum was trying to persuade me to be heavier than her – I don't know if I just imagined it, because she's always been underweight. She used to say things like, 'It doesn't matter about how heavy you are, it's the person you are that counts.' And, I'd look at her and think, It's all right for you, but it's different for *me*! I think I felt I had to be acceptable to my mum. She'd travelled a lot when she was younger, she was into politics and seemed to have got involved in lots of important issues . . . and she was slim! I just felt really envious of her but we never talked about it. I used to look at her and think, yeah, I'd love to be like her – to do all those things. That's the life I'd like to lead – I envied her. I suppose I felt if I could be very slim, she would somehow accept me more. I felt that because my views were different to hers they must be somehow wrong. If we went to restaurants to eat, I'd always wait to see how much my mum ate before I ate anything. I just constantly compared myself. I thought if I eat half of what she eats, I'll stay at the weight I want to.

At school, I was really quiet – a 'nothing'. I just didn't want to stand out. People used to mix me up with my best friend, they couldn't seem to tell the difference between us. So, I think becoming anorexic was trying to get away from all that . . . a way of being special. If I heard about anyone else being on a diet I became really angry – because that was *my* way!

Eventually, my mum got very worried about me and took me to the doctor. I thought he was conspiring against me with my mum to get me fat! He just said I didn't need to lose more weight, that I was fine the way I was. I think I must have managed to convince him I wouldn't diet anymore, so nothing happened that time. But then, during the summer my weight kept going down and down and my mum took me back to the doctor. Things were so bad by then – I only weighed five-and-a-half stone; and I had to go into hospital straight away. I thought they'd let me home immediately, but I had to stay there for a about a month. I was allowed treats – like a TV in my room, as long as my weight didn't drop. They gave me a special diet sheet which helped me to know what to eat, so I didn't panic about the amounts or what to have. I came out of hospital about a year-and-a-half ago and have been seeing a counsellor ever since, though I don't need to go as often now. I used to go every week and it really helped more than anything.

I'm still not completely better, but I'm much, much better at asserting myself now, which I could never do before. My mum used to say I was such a 'nice' child, but I never asserted myself! I'm much more open now as well. With my ex best friend – we were friends for years – I never told her anything about myself. Whereas now, with the new friend I've made, we tell each other everything!

I've noticed that everything I do now in my life is because I want to. I used to have a lot of hangups about being on my own, say at lunch times at school. I'd just hang around with people, not because I particularly liked them, but because I

> didn't want to seem unpopular or anything. But now, when my best friend does aerobics, I just go into the library on my own and do what I want to do and it feels OK. That's because it's what I want to do. I know what all my options are and I feel I can direct my life where I want it to go. I think the main thing people should realize is how long anorexia can last. It's just not worth it – *never* think it's the easy way out. I have to be true to myself now. I don't ever want to go back to the way I was.

Jane stopped eating because she wanted to feel 'special'. She envied her mother and wanted so much to be like her . . . and, of course, to be accepted by her. But although she thought to begin with that she could control her dieting, she soon realized that it was the Anorexia which was, in fact, controlling *her*. She found that very frightening, and just as difficult to cope with as all the feelings she had towards her mother and wanting to be popular at school.

Your situation may not necessarily be all that similar to Jane's but I hope you may be able to see from her story that anorexia can never solve your problems. Jane has learnt that she *is* a special person. She doesn't need to starve herelf anymore to prove this – to herself or to anyone. I hope you will be able to reach out for the help available to you before things go anywhere near as far as they did with Jane. They really don't have to in order to find what you want – and need.

5

Bulimia nervosa – What's it got to do with me?

You may be wondering why I'm including bulimia nervosa in a book about anorexia. They're two different things . . . aren't they? Well, this is true. But they are closely linked, so I feel it's important to talk about bulimia here, to explain this a bit more.

Bulimia is when people eat huge amounts of food (called bingeing) and then attempt to get rid of the food by either vomiting, taking laxatives or diuretics, which make you go to the toilet a lot. A binge is what happens when eating gets totally out of control. Many bulimics eat whatever they can lay their hands on, as quickly as possible, even food which is still frozen or raw. The food is hardly tasted, let alone enjoyed, so like Anorexia this is another way of abusing food . . . another way of abusing yourself. Many bulimics binge on high calorie carbohydrates, such as cakes, biscuits, chocolates, ice cream etc., but not all bulimics binge on these kinds of foods. The important factor is the feeling that you need to fill yourself with this food – and then get rid of it, whatever the food happens to be. A binge is very often then followed by a period of starvation, *but, unlike anorexics, bulimics are usually normal weight.*

Both bulimics and anorexics want to take control and use their eating disorder as a way of trying to take this control. For example, all the 'bits' a bulimic won't permit to be part of herself come out in vomiting and bingeing, while if you are anorexic, you will get rid of those unwanted 'bits' by not eating. These 'bits' invariably represent needs, fears, feelings you are unable to cope with.

If you are suffering from anorexia, it is possible that you, too, sometimes make yourself sick – or maybe take laxatives after you feel you've 'eaten too much'. And, of course, people who are bulimic go through periods when they starve themselves, so you can see how these two conditions are linked up.

It's important to recognzie that taking laxatives will have

absolutely no effect on your weight long term. All that happens is that you get rid of *water*, which your body will naturally make up. So as a way of controlling or losing weight, taking high amounts of laxatives is not only extremely dangerous, it doesn't help you to lose weight. Continually making yourself sick can cause mouth and throat irritations and tooth decay, and constant vomiting and laxative abuse creates severe mineral imbalance in the body. The balance of mineral salts are absolutely essential for the body to function and upsetting this balance can result in damage to the heart and kidneys and, in extreme cases, coma and death.

When I was anorexic, before seeking help, I can remember going through a stage when I believed I was getting better. This was because I suddenly found myself actually getting in touch with my 'hunger pangs'. Previously, I'd pushed them so far away into the back of my mind, I wasn't even aware of being hungry and certainly wouldn't have admitted it. Then, these hunger pangs started – and I began to raid the biscuit tin. In one sense, I believe this *was* the beginning of my recovery, because I knew then for sure that I'd been hungry for a very, very long time. But I still had a long way to go, because I felt I had no control over this hunger, or eating. So, what in fact happened was that I'd eat a whole packet of biscuits and then feel incredibly guilty, not to mention ill, afterwards. I didn't go through the bulimic bingeing and vomiting/taking laxatives stage – lots of anorexics don't – but, from my own experience as well as talking to other anorexics, these 'semi-binges' are very common. At the time, I had no idea what was happening to me. But, if it's happening to you, you could try to see it as your body responding to the way you have been depriving it of food. Surely it's a very natural reaction for it to rebel against being starved!

Coping with this new feeling of hunger isn't easy. If you are anorexic and experiencing it, you may be frightened that if you start eating you'll never be able to stop. I can assure you this won't be the case – you *can* learn to eat normally again. Many bulimics fear the same thing. They want to eat, but getting rid of the food, or starving for a few days after, is their way of controlling the situation.

Whereas if you are anorexic you will probably feel that

starving yourself gives you control over your life, people suffering from bulimia feel that their condition controls *them.* They *hate* bingeing and then ridding themselves of food, especially because it is always done secretly, making them feel even more guilty. Unlike being anorexic, where people obviously look thin, it's hard to tell if someone is bulimic, because their weight may be quite normal.

Anorexia is a means of trying to take control where your needs are not being acknowledged and met. Similarly, bulimics eat large quantities of food as a way of releasing tension caused by stress, depression, loneliness or anxiety, which hasn't been resolved. Wanting to go on a binge is a sign that you desperately need *something*, but not food. Over-eating is your way of trying to fill a gap left by your emotional needs. The 'controlling' part is getting rid of the food, in other words controlling whether or not it stays inside. In the same way that you may as an anorexic feel that you are somehow 'trapped' by your desire to continue starving, people with bulimia are trapped in a vicious circle of bingeing and starving, or bingeing and somehow getting rid of what's been eaten.

If you recognize that binge eating is your way of coping with anything which worries you, whether it's an emotional upset, pressure at school, boredom, or just the feeling that nothing is going right, you will be taking the first step towards recovery.

The only way to stop the cycle of bingeing is to begin to eat regularly – little and often – including carbohydrates every day. The more you deprive yourself of this food, the more you are likely to binge on it eventually.

One *Just Seventeen* reader wrote to say how difficult she was finding it to stop bingeing:

> I seem to be dieting for days on end, cutting out bread, potatoes – anything I consider to be fattening – and then I go on a massive binge, consisting of all the fattening things I haven't been eating. It's stupid really, because I just end up feeling so disgusted with myself and then I go on another diet. I get such bad cravings, though, I can never keep up the diets for long. Please help me . . .

Please remember that whether you are bulimic or anorexic,

depriving yourself of food will quite likely make you want to binge. Try very hard to acknowledge that what you are doing just doesn't work – and it's very, very dangerous. It doesn't make the problems go away, it just gives you yet another one to cope with. This will not only make you feel even worse about yourself, but it can also have serious long-term physical consequences.

Both anorexia and bulimia are potentially life-threatening conditions and both are ways of avoiding the *real* problems underneath. Self-induced vomiting and laxative abuse are particularly dangerous and you will be losing control, not gaining it, if you continue to harm yourself in this way.

I can't pretend there is an overnight cure for either anorexia or bulimia, but what I can assure you of is this: recovery means facing up to ways of coping other than starving, bingeing, or laxative abuse. It means learning how to eat without feeling guilty or frightened. Most of all, it means finding the courage to confront all those feelings of anger, depression, loneliness, fear, lack of self-confidence and confusion about growing up. As I've said previously, it can be a difficult and very gradual process, but reaching out for the help available will mean that you can find the way towards recovery and break out of the cycle of bingeing and starving once and for all.

6

Carol's story

I've had a pretty hard life, though not as bad as some people's. I guess there's always somebody worse off than you. Since I was three years old my dad worked abroad and mum looked after me and my brother who is two years older than me. I hardly ever saw my dad, so I grew up without the proper love of my dad. Mum went through a hard time, because they used to argue a lot before he went away. When I was about nine my mum asked me if I would mind if they got divorced. She'd had enough! I told her if that's what she needed, then it was OK with me, though they didn't get divorced for a long time. My dad packed in his job abroad and came home and we all moved into a pub together. I was eleven then. Mum and dad were still arguing, though behind my back. When we moved to the pub we had to leave behind a beautiful home and I had to leave my friends and school which was awful. Then after a couple of years we moved to another pub, in yet another strange town. But dad wanted to move on, so we all had to. I had no friends in the new village because I had to go to school somewhere else. It was hell. While we were living there, mum and dad had a massive row and she walked out. She found another man! At first I had to live with my dad and it was awful because he was so strict, but eventually my mum found a house with her boyfriend big enough for me and my brother to move into. We got on well with mum's boyfriend. But picking up our things from dad was terrible. We were both in tears – he and mum had been together for eighteen years.

Then my favourite grandad died, which just about finished me off. I had the chance to go to his funeral, but I couldn't face it. I only found out a year ago that he had been cremated. I would have liked to have been able to visit him and I still cry to this very day. It's hard to believe he's dead.

My dad now lives with his new girlfriend and her children and he really seems to have changed for the better now.

I first started putting weight on around this time and began bingeing etc. Mum's really changed and always seems to stick up for her boyfriend. I seem to argue with him a lot these days. During this time, I had a couple of boyfriends who treated me very badly, one of them even beat me up.

I hate my body. I do eat quite a lot especially when I'm depressed, worried or bored. I've tried just about every diet on the market, but they haven't worked for one reason or another. I haven't got much confidence any more. I started to make myself sick after these binges, but that just makes me feel worse. I used to exercise but, then I stopped because I never seem to have the energy any more. I always seem tired. I also get bad food cravings, but I'm not pregnant.

I just want to feel happy about my weight and not have to worry about dieting and making myself sick any more . . .

I think Carol's story is a good example of someone who has tried to push away her feelings of rejection, loneliness and unhappiness by turning to food for comfort and to block out these painful emotions. But, as you can see, her bouts of over-eating followed by vomiting are just making it even more difficult for her to get in touch with all those feelings. So, in a way, Carol delays coping with difficult feelings and parts of herself she can't confront and puts food in their place. But this just makes her feel worse still.

Carol needs help and support to begin facing these emotions and coming to terms with what has happened in the past. She needs to begin accepting that she is a worthwhile person and that she has things other than a binge to turn to. Because a binge is a bulimic's way of replacing all the other needs she/he is denying.

Whether you are bulimic like Carol – or anorexic – it's OK to go through times in your life when you can't cope alone and need to ask for help.

PART TWO

Taking Action

7

Asking for help

Accepting something's wrong

So far in this book, we've looked at ways in which you can begin to understand what anorexia is all about and the harm it can cause. If you have read so far, I assume it's because anorexia in some way plays a part in your life.

It's important to recognize that if you suffer from anorexia, the very first crucial step towards recovery is both acknowledging and accepting that something is wrong. This is a positive and brave step, so never underestimate the achievement in being able to say 'I need help . . .' I can't emphasize strongly enough that by doing so you will be opening up a whole new life for yourself – one which is full of opportunities, choices and the freedom you have so far been denying yourself.

Accepting that something is wrong isn't the loss of control you may inwardly fear it is. In fact, it is the very opposite. Because while you are locked inside your thoughts of starving, counting calories, over-exercising and more starving, you are well and truly trapped and your life remains very limited indeed. The point of acceptance will undoubtedly seem a very difficult and even frightening stage. Anorexia may well have been your 'safety net' now for some time. It's something familiar, something you feel you can rely on to get you by. Starving has meant accepting that something is wrong means finding the courage to 'let go'.

As I've said before, you may fear that without your anorexic way of thinking you won't have anything else to think about. After all, your entire attention has probably been taken up with one thing, and one thing only . . . the job of not eating. Therefore, it's hardly surprising that you start believing there's nothing else you can do.

But the truth is, there *is* so much more you have of value to offer to yourself. Once you can begin to realize that what's happening just isn't good for you, you have opened up the door which can lead to recovery and a way out of what's happening. Most important of all, it can lead you to a far happier way of being.

Asking for help isn't going to be easy. I remember thinking that it was '*my*' anorexia and I didn't want anybody to take it away! At the same time, I really desperately wanted to let go of it and, thankfully, it was that feeling which won over. It can be hard to realize what a tight grip you've allowed anorexia to have over you – taking away your freedom, your right to make choices . . . your life, if you let it.

How to go about it and what happens

The first and most obvious choice of someone to confide in is a close member of your family. Chances are they have been standing by feeling very helpless and if you approach them you are, in a sense, giving them permission to help you. You are also giving yourself permission to start caring for *yourself* . . . and this is what matters more than anything in the world.

Even if you can't exactly explain to your parents what's wrong, you can ask for their support in making contact with a doctor or with an organization. If you feel you *really* can't tell your parents or guardians, there are still options open to you. Remember, there *are* people who will understand and can offer support and help. I will explain here the steps you can take to find that help and what to expect.

Your own doctor

Obvious though this sounds, many people tend to forget that your own doctor always has access to other specialists in your area, so this is a good starting point. Response from GPs varies from one to another. For instance, it's as well to be realistic and acknowledge that *some* doctors may say something along the lines of 'snap out of it', or suggest that all you need is a diet sheet. However, this *shouldn't* happen – it's definitely not the response you need and there's no reason for you to accept such an approach. *If this happens to you, see another doctor.*

You can do this in several ways:

- If it's a group practice, simply ask to see another doctor in that practice.
- Practices also often have counsellors, health visitors or nurses attached to them, so you can ask what's available. (You can do this anyway, if this appeals to you more than talking to your doctor.)
- Change your doctor completely. This is a simple process, so there's absolutely no need to worry about doing it if, for whatever reason, you no longer wish to be registered with your current doctor. All you need to do is choose a new doctor – by asking around friends, family, or someone living locally who can recommend a good sympathetic GP. Go to the new surgery and say you want to register with that particular doctor. Your notes will automatically be forwarded from your previous doctor. The new doctor you choose must be within the boundary area, but it's obviously to your advantage in any case to choose someone close to where you live. *Most importantly you should look out for a doctor who's prepared to understand. It's your right – and you deserve it.*

Hints about going to your doctor

Before you go to the surgery, it may help you to write a brief account of what's been happening. This will give you a bit more confidence and will also be very useful to your doctor in understanding the situation. If you have been anorexic for a while and know full well that you can't just 'go away and eat three meals a day' make it absolutely clear that you can't manage on your own. Don't be afraid to explain to your doctor that a diet sheet alone won't help you – you need counselling as well.

You may be tempted to pretend you *can* eat sensibly without any further help if he/she just tells you what to eat. You know as well as I do that this *may* possibly convince your doctor . . . but, who would you really be kidding?

Remember, too, that you are perfectly within your rights to ask if you have any preference towards seeing a female doctor in a group practice – whether *you* are male or female. Ultimately, though, if someone has a tolerant, understanding and sympathetic approach, with a good insight into the problems of anorexia, their gender isn't important.

What's likely to happen when you go to your doctor?

You must expect to be weighed and to stop losing weight. It's important to realize that no doctor helping you to overcome anorexia will ignore weight, so try very hard to accept this. What it *doesn't* mean is that people will expect you to get bigger and bigger – they won't. But if you continue to lose weight you then make it far more difficult to be in control of your recovery, because dropping to a dangerous weight means people will have quite literally to step in and save your life. *It's far, far better to ask for help before things go too far.*

It's possible that your doctor may be able to offer you some counselling himself/herself. Obviously, if you feel comfortable about this, then you will probably find this supportive and helpful, certainly in the short term. However, the reality is that many GPs simply don't have the time or resources to offer counselling sessions to their patients on a regular basis. If this is the case with your own doctor, or if he or she simply feels they are unable to offer you all the help you need, then they may be able to refer you. This could be to someone attached to the docter's practice if available, or you may otherwise be referred to a hospital as an *outpatient.*

It's important that you continue to see your own doctor, as well as having counselling.

Some hospitals have special adolescent units and family therapy departments, so your doctor may refer you to one of these places, if available in your area. Most areas do have psychology services which can be very helpful. If you are under 16, it's very likely that you will be referred to your area's Child and Adolescent Psychiatry Service for treatment. Alternatively, you may be referred to a paediatrician (a medical doctor who treats children and young people) and/or a dietician. Some dieticians can be very helpful and can teach you to eat sensibly again to gain some weight, or at least stop losing weight.

If possible, try to talk about these options with your GP, but at the very least check with him/her to make sure that you are absolutely clear about who you are going to see.

Don't be afraid to ask questions!

If you are given a choice, consider counselling seriously, because this will help you to talk about the kinds of problems you've been experiencing, and, far more importantly, will help you to identify what the problems actually are. But don't forget that you will also need help with your weight and eating. No reputable counsellor will continue to see someone who is literally wasting away before their eyes.

What happens if you are referred to a Child and Adolescent Psychiatric Unit

If you are referred to a Child and Adolescent Psychiatry Unit you will probably be seen with your parents and you may also be given individual therapy which you can ask for. Someone will talk to you and your family to see what kind of difficulties and problems you are having, so that your family can help you – and also get help themselves if necessary. Because anorexia very often goes hand-in-hand with family problems, it obviously makes sense that you receive help in confronting these difficulties together. This doesn't mean your family's at fault – or that you've done something wrong either. In life people experience all kinds of problems and difficult feelings involving close relationships and sometimes not only the person who becomes ill is involved, especially where anorexia is concerned.

It's not a question of blame, it's about learning to understand, acknowledge and find new ways of coping . . . both as an individual and as a family together.

A point about seeing a counsellor, psychiatrist or therapist, if your doctor refers you, is that these people are simply the kind of doctors who can help with emotional feelings and problems, rather than a physical pain in some part of your body. Some young people look upon psychiatrists and therapy as something to do with being 'mad' or 'weird' but this is a very out-dated and inaccurate description of this kind of medical help. Lots of people seek counselling at some time in their lives – not only because of anorexia, but for all kinds of emotional problems. There's absolutely nothing to be ashamed of. If you're ill something hurts, you go to an ordinary doctor. If you're upset or unhappy about something and it's affecting you in a physical way it makes sense to see a specialist who can help with this kind of problem.

What happens if you are referred to a paediatrician?

A paediatrician will diagnose and treat any medical complications, advise on diet (probably referring you to a dietician) and may admit you to a medical ward, *if necessary*. However, this isn't likely to happen if you seek help early before things have gone too far.

What happens if you are referred to a dietician?

A dietician will ask about what you are eating. Try to be honest about this and mention any behaviour designed to control your weight – over-exercising, counting calories, etc. The idea will probably be first to try to stop you losing weight, then gradually increase weight if you are willing. If you are not willing to do this, you should make it clear right away if you can. *Remember, no one can help you if you have a completely different aim in mind from theirs.*

This kind of treatment is more likely to involve advice concerning your diet, with less attention given to problems.

Again, you will be asked to stop losing weight and given a special diet sheet, listing all the foods you should eat each day, with portions and quantities clearly given. *It's important that you know exactly what to eat and when. Ask for this information if it's not given.*

Remember, although a decision about where you will be referred is basically up to your GP, you can ask for counselling, as well as dietary advice and help.

People you can talk to

- At school
  If you are still at school it's quite possible that there will be a school nurse so you can ask to see her. Nurses attached to schools are often familiar with eating disorders, so this is another good starting point.
- At college
  If you are a college student, there is very likely to be a

counsellor attached to the college, or someone to whom you can be referred. Ask your principal if there is a doctor attached to the college health service, because again these doctors are often used to seeing people with anorexia and other eating disorders.

- An adult you can trust
  It may be the case that you feel easier about confiding in someone who isn't a doctor to begin with. This is far better than not telling anyone and is likely to give you the support you need to seek further help when you feel ready to do so. Make sure that it's someone you feel very comfortable with – someone you trust and like. There's little point in approaching an adult you don't generally have some kind of bond with. Someone like a teacher or youth club leader, for example, is more likely to have some experience in helping people in your situation.

If you are desperate, you can always go to the Casualty Dept. of your local hospital, where you will be seen by a paediatrician or psychiatrist.

Fear of asking for help

You may be afraid to tell your doctor or school nurse – or anyone else for that matter – that you need help in case you are taken into hospital. I do understand this fear. However, this is where you can make the decision to ask for help before things go too far, because it is only when your weight is dangerously low that you are likely to be admitted to hospital. *In most cases, people with anorexia can be helped without being taken into hospital.*

Refusing help . . . what can happen and how to avoid it

Because your recovery largely depends on you acknowledging and accepting something's wrong – and asking for help – it's also important to acknowledge that when you are a child, you can be put into hospital against your will, if your parents request this, even if you are over the age of sixteen. This isn't because people are against you, hate you or are ganging up against you – or because they want you to get fat. It's because they care and quite simply don't want you to die.

If you ask for help early you can avoid the situation where people take over and decide your rights. *You can be in control if you act early and ask for help before things get out of hand.* Unless you're really physically at risk, very few hospitals will admit a young person. So please don't allow the fear of this happening stop you from seeing a doctor.

Why not get in touch with. . . ?

Apart from the kinds of ways I've mentioned of reaching out for help, I can also recommend getting in touch with the following organization:

- *Eating Disorders Association* – EDA (address and phone number on p.108).
  This is a nationwide organization which can give you lots of help, support, advice and understanding in the way of self-help groups in your area, helplines, fact sheets, newsletters and booklists. This organization can also offer support to your family so that they can understand what kind of help you need from them.
  The EDA can also refer you to other specialists if necessary, or individuals they feel can best help you. They are extremely sympathetic and professional, and can give you the support you need in coping and in learning to recover. All you have to do is write or telephone and they will send you the information you need.
- *Anorexia and Bulimia Care* (address and phone numbers on p.108).
  If you are interested in contacting a Christian organization you can get in touch with Anorexia and Bulimia Care. You don't have to be a Christian to get in touch with them: they even have two separate sets of information sheets – one with quotes from the Bible and the other for people who are not interested in the religious aspect. They basically believe that a link with Christianity for some people can offer extra support, but they don't discriminate between 'believers' and 'non-believers'. They can provide a list of resources, help sheets, tapes to help self-esteem and tapes on ex-sufferers explaining how they got better. In addition, there are one or two books to borrow or buy

and a book recommendation list. Unfortunately, they don't have groups nationwide, although they do run one or two groups in limited areas. You can also fill in a form to be put in touch with a carer in your area. Write or phone for further information.

- *NAYPCAS*
  Another possibility open to you is independently to contact an organization called NAYPCAS – National Association of Young People's Counselling and Advisory Service, 17–23 Albion Street, Leicester LE1 6GD (enclose a stamped addressed envelope when you write). You can write asking for details of your nearest youth Counselling and Advisory Service. This service is free and completely confidential. Once you are sent an address (or addresses), it would be up to you to contact the counselling and advisory service in question for an appointment. (However, some of these places do operate on a walk-in basis, so an appointment may not be necessary.) Youth Counselling centres are invariably run in an informal, friendly atmosphere and you will be given the opportunity to talk to a counsellor on a regular basis, in complete confidence.
- *Saneline* (Freephone) 0171–724 8000, lines open 2 p.m. – midnight *every day of the year.*
  This is a telephone helpline you may ring if you are concerned about an eating disorder or have any kind of problem and want to talk about how you are feeling.
- Finally, don't forget you can ring any of the other helplines – such as Childline, Careline or the Samaritans (Details and phone numbers on Page 109) if you need someone sympathetic to confide in.

The main thing to remember is that if you ask for help you have taken a very brave and positive step and this, in itself, is a huge achievement.

8

Making progress and coping with setbacks

Nobody can wave a magic wand and make things suddenly change. You need time. Getting better is a very gradual process. There will be times when you seem to be taking steps forwards – and times when you may feel you are making no progress at all, or even going backwards. *That's OK.* You may have been anorexic for a long time, so it stands to reason you won't suddenly make a miraculous recovery – nor will it be easy. Accepting that this is the case will help you to be kinder to yourself. Expecting too much, too soon, will just put more unnecessary demands on you, which you don't need! Most of all you will need to *want* things to change.

If you are receiving some kind of outside help along the lines mentioned in the previous chapter, you will be expected to put on weight. This sounds very obvious, I know, but when you are anorexic it's one of the most difficult things in the world to agree to and accept. But having come this far in asking for help, you will probably realize that you need to place some trust in your helpers. So, putting on weight doesn't mean that you'll be expected to become *over*weight – or even put on unrealistic pounds. What it does mean is that you will need to aim at either the weight you were beforehand – if that's considered to be an OK weight for you – or at least a weight at which your periods are likely to start again. Remember, your periods have stopped because you have been starving yourself and when they start again very much depends upon whether you eat normally. You are unlikely to start your periods again if you continue to eat only low fat diet foods. Your periods are the best guide as to what's happening. When they come back and are regular it means that your body is functioning properly again.

It's important to acknowledge that until you gain weight you will be unable to identify what the real problems are – let alone be able to resolve them. So, try to accept that putting on some weight and accepting that something is wrong are two very important steps in your recovery. You will need to include things like cheese, nuts, pulses and carbohydrates in your diet, so it's a good idea to ask a dietician or your doctor or hospital for advice about this. Most dieticians will be happy to tell you exactly what to eat and how much, which will be helpful for you to begin with. As you've probably discovered, being anorexic makes it very difficult – if not impossible – for you to make decisions about how much is too much and how much is too little when it comes to food. So guidance in this area is a good start. Later I hope you will find it possible to throw diet sheets away and trust your own judgement, appetite and needs! But, as I've said, you should take things slowly step by step.

Here are some checkpoints you may find useful

1. Set some *realistic* goals for yourself. Try not to think that if something goes wrong it means you've failed. It doesn't! Think of some things you'd like to do in the future, however small they may seem. Being positive about this will give you something other than food to think about.

2. Focus on what you can and have achieved, rather than blame yourself for setbacks. Remember, you can learn a lot from them and then move on from there.

3. You may fear that things will be awful when you start to put on weight, but they won't feel so bad if you ask for all the support you need – from family, friends and any professional help you're receiving. When you put on weight, what *will* happen is that you will, in a sense, get back some of the anxiety that was passed onto those close to you when you were thin. But this is only a temporary discomfort and one which will pass as you begin to get better. What you need to remind yourself over and over again is that none of these difficult feelings will last and they are far more preferable to the anxieties, fears and despair which accompany anorexia.

4. Make some decisions about mealtimes with your family. Mealtimes can remain very difficult for you unless you try to take some control over the situation – but, in a different way than before. This time negotiate with your parents/guardians about

whether or not you would like *them* to decide when and what you eat. This can make a big difference to you, because you want to let someone else decide for a while, until you feel more confident. Or it may feel more comfortable to plan your favourite foods with your mum. Talk about this together and see how you feel. You may even want to try both ways – and then decide. The main thing is that you have some kind of structure around mealtimes so you don't feel anxious about them.

5. Other people eating may be a problem for you to begin with, but this will gradually get easier. It may be tempting to look at other people's plates and use them as a measure as to how much – or how little *you* should eat. But this is a time for you to try to concentrate on eating the amounts which are right for you at the moment. Remember, you will need to slowly learn how to get back in touch with proper feelings of being hungry – and having had enough to eat. Most people are able to take these feelings very much for granted and can rely on them to tell them when to eat. But, when you are anorexic, you push these feelings away to such an extent that it's a question of time and practice before you can expect them to fully return.

So, for now, sticking to diet sheets provided by your doctor/dietician or paediatrician can be helpful. Eventually you will be able to throw them all away and rely on recognizing your own needs.

6. Many anorexics do feel intense hunger much of the time but push these feelings away and won't admit to even having them. You may then fear that if you start eating you won't be able to stop. Please be asured that this fear is very common, so try not to imagine that something terrible is about to happen if you eat. It won't. Take advantge of all the support offered to you to help you through these fears.

7. There may be mealtimes when you genuinely feel you can't eat. Again, these feelings are very common while you're getting better. This is probably because you are feeling worried and uneasy about things getting out of control, but, if you try to eat what's been agreed as 'your portion', you will find that you are gradually able to trust yourself more and more.

8. *Occasional bingeing is normal!* Most people will be able to

tell you of the time they ate a whole packet of biscuits or whatever. Try not to panic if this happens to you while you are recovering. It's not a sign that you've 'failed', or that something's going terribly wrong. Also, the more you deprive yourself of food, the more likely you are to want to go on binges. It's a perfectly natural reaction to not giving yourself enough of the right kinds of foods. It's important that you continue to eat properly even if you've binged. If you skip a meal just because you feel you've overeaten, you will only be continuing your old patterns.

9. Talk to close family/friends about what's happening and try to explain how you feel. For instance, if you know there are certain things which make you feel uncomfortable at the moment, say so. Other people can't begin to understand how vulnerable you are unless you tell them. If, for instance, it makes you feel uneasy if people comment on the fact that you've eaten all your dinner, explain beforehand that it's easier for you if they don't draw attention to what you eat.

10. You may feel anxious if someone says something like 'You're looking well'. This is invariably a completely innocent comment, but you may well take it to mean 'You're looking fatter'. Try to remind yourself that for all the time you've been starving yourself, you've most probably looked anything but 'well' – even though you thought you looked OK. Try very hard to accept such comments in a more positive and complimentary light, without reading something else into them. But, again, it helps if you can explain to people if something makes you feel uncomfortable. In time, things like this won't bother you any more, because you will gradually feel more comfortable about yourself. Chance remarks are just that – it helps not to take them too much to heart.

Exercise – learning to let go

While you are anorexic, you will probably feel the necessity to take lots of exercise in an attempt to burn off even more calories and weight. Try to accept that this is a symptom of your anorexic condition and you will need to let go of it gradually in order to recover. It's probably a frightening thought because over-exercising can be another way of blocking out feelings and needs. Try to be honest with whoever is helping you to get better, so that you receive support in aiming to cut down on the amount of exercise you're taking. If your weight is dangerously low, be prepared to give up exercising altogether for a while, until you stop losing weight.

Remember, the more you exercise the more 'fuel' you need in your body – not the other way round! No professional athlete in his/her right mind would dream of taking the kind of strenuous 'training' undertaken by an anorexic without eating a good, nourishing, balanced diet. You don't need to do punishing 'workouts' every day in order to stay fit. Exercise is something you should enjoy in moderation to stay *healthy* . . . not something inflicted on yourself to the point of utter exhaustion.

Being anorexic has been your way of blocking out difficult feelings. As you start making progress towards recovery, you will need to accept that you may feel anxious – even frightened – about confronting these feelings. Again, give yourself time and try not to expect everything to come right straight away.

Finally, many anorexics think greed is absolutely disgusting because you may associate it only with food. It can then be very hard for you to acknowledge that you have any feelings at all of this kind. But a certain amount of greed is natural, even necessary, in life – such as greed for love or perhaps ambition. These are normal feelings and are all part of your needs as a human being, ones you've turned your back on while you've been anorexic.

PART THREE

Coping With Stress Without Starving

In this section, we're going to look at the different kinds of problems you may be experiencing. Many people have written to me about such problems, telling me that they've stopped eating because of them.

This isn't meant to be an A–Z guide. If your particular problem isn't included here it doesn't mean it's not important – or without a solution. My aim is to try to show you how you can find ways of confronting your problems, needs and feelings and finding help and support, instead of resorting to self-destructive behaviour as a means of coping. Becoming anorexic, or even just going on a diet, in an attempt to deal with difficult emotions and situations in any area of your life won't give you the kind of control you really want or need. What it does is push things under the surface where they remain unresolved, giving you an extra problem to cope with.

Looking at constructive ways of facing problems and reaching out for available support is the first step towards finding new ways of coping. So far, anorexia has been your way of avoiding this, but try very hard to acknowledge that while you allow food to rule your life you can never be really content and happy. It's important to find other ways of expressing your needs and making sure they are met.

9

What do you really need?

> My life reads like an open book
> for all and sundry to take a look.
> This is not how I want it to be,
> for my life belongs to me.
> At times I feel the need to be
> reassured by the person closest to me . . .
>
> A poem by Nicola Stobie (aged 19)

We all need love and reassurance and, most of all, I think, we all need to be accepted for who and what we are. One of the things I remember most about being anorexic is the feeling of wanting to be an individual. Starving is one drastic way of getting attention and standing out as being 'different', but it's also a very self-destructive and therefore ineffective way of being 'you'. Perhaps you see yourself as some kind of failure, someone who, in your own eyes and maybe those of others, just doesn't come up to the high standard you expect of yourself?

As well as wanting to be an individual, it's quite possible that you will also want to be able to lean on your family and be protected by them. So, how on earth can you be an independent person as well as asking for love and protection? Maybe you feel that you can only ask for one or the other and so not eating for you somehow resolves this two-way problem?

For example, by starving yourself you may imagine that you are taking control of the 'part' of yourself which wants to be an individual – and an independent person. But by starving you also become an *ill* person who needs attention and depends on family for support. I'm not trying to tell you this is a *conscious* decision that you sit down and make one day, but giving it some thought now may help you to see that there are, at least, two needs you could have been afraid to face before.

First of all, you 'need' to try to accept and like yourself. Nobody is perfect and trying to achieve perfection is almost like setting yourself up . . . for failure. So try to look at the things you can count as your positive strengths and know that weaknesses are part of being a human being – not a sign that you are worthless or not good enough.

To some extent, most people like to feel they can live up to other people's expectations, *but*, and this is a huge but, there comes a point when you have to acknowledge that what other people expect of you isn't always realistic! You cannot happily go through your life trying to please everyone else, when the one person who isn't being satisfied is *you*. As I've said, most of us want to gain the respect of others, but the price to pay should never be your own needs.

From all the hundreds of letters I've received, I realize how difficult it is for many people to cope with the various aspects of growing up. Earlier I mentioned the kinds of problems many young people have written about. Now let's take a closer look at the kinds of problems which seem to worry you most. The kinds of problems which often result in self-destructive behaviour such as not eating or harming yourself in other ways.

10

Lack of self-confidence, shyness and loneliness

Earlier in the book, I said that I felt these three problems often seem to go hand in hand for you. You feel self-conscious and shy and so avoid the kind of social contact which is likely to bring you new friends. Put like that it sounds very straightforward, but I'm well aware that lacking self-confidence can be a painful experience for many young people.

I believe the very first step for any of you who lack a feeling of self-worth – and also feel very shy – is to spend some time trying to re-value yourself. Basically, shyness is all about low self-esteem and not thinking you are able to contribute anything worthwhile to a friendship, a conversation or whatever. OK. So there are some people who are brainier than others . . . some are prettier . . . others have a great sense of humour. You, too, have got something to offer, something you can share with other people. Your shyness may stem from the fact that you underrate your looks. I've lost count of the number of letters I've received from people who describe themselves as 'ugly'.

One letter in particular has stayed in my mind. It was accompanied by a photograph of two 14-year-old girls. I looked at the picture before reading the letter and my very first reaction was how very pretty these two girls looked. I then read the letter, which was from one of the girls – they were sisters. She described herself in such a negative way that I thought she must have sent a photo of someone else! In no way was her description an accurate one of herself. She saw her face, hair and figure as 'a disaster'. I could only see an extremely attractive girl, sitting next to another attractive girl.

I think the problem arises between, say, best friends or even sisters, when you start comparing yourself and thinking you don't match up to what you see as pretty or interesting. But we are all individuals and just because you are different from the class favourite, it doesn't mean you're 'ugly' or 'boring'. Putting yourself down like that will only help to increase feelings of shyness, self-consciousness and isolation.

Many people have written to me saying they never meet any new friends and stay in every weekend or evening, hanging around doing nothing, feeling more and more lonely and unhappy. This then becomes a vicious circle, because it's hardly likely you'll meet anyone new if the furthest you ever venture is to the bathroom and back!

First of all, try to learn to like yourself and begin to enjoy your own company. I say this because if you go out desperately seeking friends when you can't stand yourself, there's much less chance the other people will be drawn towards you. In many ways, other people pick up from *you* what they need to know. For instance, if you have a mole on your face and allow this to increase your shyness by always pulling your hair over your face, you will simply be drawing more attention to something which may otherwise not seem important. Similarly, if you're going through a spotty stage and allow this to be all you ever think about, you are far less likely to want to go out and meet people.

On the other hand, if you take an interest in what people are talking about and talk about things which interest you, whether or not you've got spots, a mole, a scar or a brace won't seem that important!

Remember, if you come across people who themselves draw attention to these things by picking on you or calling you names, this tells you something about *them* – not you. It tells you they're immature, insensitive and probably trying to boost their own self-image by putting you down. So, never allow this kind of thing to influence the way you feel about facing people with confidence.

> A girl once wrote to me with what I think is a brilliant idea for overcoming feelings of low self-esteem. She told me she wrote down a list of all her 'good' points – and then, on the other side of the paper, all her 'bad' points. The first attempt made her feel even worse because she automatically found enough 'bad' points to fill a book, but was short on the other side of the list. It didn't look a very impressive sight, and it

actually made her realize just how negative she had become about herself. She screwed up the list and started again, including all the things she wanted to do and all the various plans she wanted to make for her life. The list looked a whole lot better after that!

So why not try to make your own list, even if it means more than one attempt. Everyone has got something to offer and I'm certain you've got many positive things if you really think about it. Even if it's an ambition of some kind – that counts! It's something about you that other people can relate to and find interesting.

One thing which many people seem to overlook when they suffer from shyness is that most people experience shyness to some extent. Don't be fooled into thinking that everyone who gives the impression of being very 'cool' and self-confident actually is. They're not! Also, when you're talking to someone, it's easy to start worrying too much about whether you're saying the right thing or being good enough company. The fact is that most people are far too involved in what *they* want to say to be at all concerned with that. A good way to overcome your feelings of shyness is to concentrate on the other person. Really listen to what they're saying; ask questions, take an interest in what they're talking about. That way, you tend to stop focusing on whether or not you're going to go bright red, or get your words jumbled up. Besides, blushing and tripping up on your words isn't a crime. It'll pass and if you stay calm and continue to tune-in to what your friend's saying, you'll find blushing becomes less and less of a problem.

Take some time to think about some activities you'd like to get involved in where you are also likely to meet new people. Whether or not you're dead keen on sport, I always think sports centres are great places for meeting people. You don't have to aim for being a champion badminton player or swimmer, but there may be at least one sport or class you can enjoy. Some centres even have yoga classes, and yoga is a great way of keeping fit and learning how to calm down and relax. The more relaxed you feel, the more likely you are to overcome feelings of shyness. Sports clubs or centres usually also organize social events, so that's something else you can get involved in. There are so many different activities you can enjoy – anything from skating to dance classes, learning to take photographs to cycling. It all depends on what interests *you*. One thing's for sure. If you encourage yourself to become involved in even just one new interest, it will bring you in touch with other people of your own age who enjoy the same kinds of things as you. This means that straight away you have at least one thing in common. Whether it's a swimming club or learning how to act, you're bound to make one new friend. You can ask at your local public library about local clubs and activities for people of your age group.

Trying to break out of the vicious circle of not being able to face meeting new people and becoming more shy and lonely will increase your self-confidence. Take it gradually – don't expect too much of yourself to begin with – and be pleased with your achievements, however small they may seem to you. Making an effort is worth it!

Recommended books

- Dr Phyllis Shaw, *Meeting People is Fun – How to overcome shyness (Sheldon)*
- Dr Paul Hauck, *How to Be Your Own Best Friend* (Sheldon)
- Don Gabor, *How to Start a Conversation and Make Friends* (Sheldon) Supportive and encouraging advice.
- Dianne Doubtfire, *Overcoming Shyness – A Woman's Guide* (Sheldon)

These books aim to help you to build your self-confidence and think more positively about yourself.

Contacts for making friends

- *Youth Clubs UK*
  Keswick House, 30 Peacock Lane, Leicester LE1 5NY. Tel. 0533–629514. Contact them to find out about youth clubs in your area.

Contacts for help

- *Careline*
  Tel. 0181–514 1177
  Sympathetic and confidential helpline for all young people.

- *Samaritans*
  Listed in your local telephone directory, 24-hour confidential helpline. Non-judgemental, sympathetic towards young people, willing to listen. It can sometimes be possible to arrange for you to talk to a counsellor face-to-face.

11

I'm feeling depressed . . .

'My life's a complete mess and I don't feel I've got anything to live for . . .'

These are words I've read many times in your letters and it always saddens me to think that at the time of writing, the sender honestly feels there's absolutely no way out of this unhappy state. You may have been told over and over again that you'll 'grow out of it' or 'it's just a phase', but you want to know how that's going to help you *now*.

First, adolescence *is* a great time of change and development, with lots of different kinds of emotions to deal with. One minute you're going to feel 'up' and see everything in a good light, the next minute you escape to your room in a mood so awful that the slightest remark from your mum or dad will have you in floods of tears. You probably feel that nobody in the world can possibly understand what it's like. You may think it'll never get better and you may be wondering 'Why *me*?'

It's natural and normal to experience these ups and downs. Although it becomes extremely boring to be told this over and over again, these moods *are* all part of growing up. But what if you feel so 'down' that you feel unable to get on with things, or cope with what's happening? You may feel so bad that not eating (or eating too much) may seem like a good way of either blocking out these emotions, or allowing you tou feel that you can, at least, be in charge of *something* – what you do or don't eat. If you try to deal with feelings of depression by starving yourself, you will only ultimately increase your sense of powerlessness when you begin to realize that starving in itself forces you into a corner of boring repetition. In other words, you end up with less *real* control over your life – not more.

As an anorexic, you may not necessarily become depressed, but when you begin to gain weight and think about recovery it's inevitable that you will be faced with new feelings of being helpless or feelings that things are hopeless. If you can try to recognize this as a part of your recovery and get the support you need in understanding what's happening, this stage in your recovery will seem less threatening and difficult.

Many people feel very pressurized by GCSEs and other exams. If this is your experience, you may imagine that everyone but you is coping. It's very easy to become isolated with these fears, and then it can seem they are absolutely insurmountable. Not eating may then become your way of trying to push these feelings of stress away. Try to acknowledge that a lot of young people find studying and exams a stressful time. It's nothing to be ashamed of. If you can try to talk about how you feel – either to a teacher you get along with and trust, your parents, close family friend or relative, or one of the special helpline counsellors – you will find this will take a great weight off your shoulders. Sharing how you feel with someone who understands and can offer you support will help ease the burden you may feel simply because you are no longer attempting to deal with the situation on your own. There may well be ways in which you can reduce the stress. I always feel it's a good idea to try to get a balance between studying and leisure time. Too much of one and you will feel the ill-effect. Try to put aside a certain set amount of time each week in which to study, and then make sure that you allow yourself some time to enjoy yourself too. It's really a question of balance and if your parents can see that you're being sensible about it and not staying out late every night, I'm sure they will try to support you in what you're doing.

Any decision you make concerning your choice of subjects or career isn't irreversible. If you change your mind at some point, it doesn't mean you've failed. Lots of things can influence these decisions, so try to give yourself some leeway and you're far more likely to feel less panicked and restricted.

Learning to relax is also very important if you are feeling depressed or under any kind of stress. There are some very basic relaxation techniques you can learn which can help to keep you calm. They work well not only at the time you are actually doing them, but when you find yourself becoming tense you can put what you've learnt into practice. Some people find that yoga and meditation really help them to calm down, so it's certainly worth looking into this to see if something like this may suit you. Your local public library should have books and tapes on relaxation and should be able to advise you about yoga classes in your area. You could also try asking at your school/college because your P.E. instructor may well be able to advise you.

Talking about how you feel is one of the best ways of learning to cope with your depression and mixed emotions and will help you to feel less isolated. Remember that telephone helplines and counselling centres are there to help young people who need support and to be listened to. It's important for you to understand this. You're worth the time – you're worth being listened to . . . and you're worth the commitment which is invested into running these helplines especially for people like you. There's no one answer on how to cope with feeling 'down'. You're an individual and can expect to be treated as such if you contact one of these counselling services. Remember, too, that the people who run them are sympathetic and understanding, and you can talk to them in complete confidence.

If you do feel you can confide in a parent, guardian, close relative, friend of the family, or perhaps a teacher you can trust, this a good first move. Try not to bottle up your feelings until you become overwhelmed by how you feel. Sometimes writing your thoughts down on paper can be very helpful. Somehow, getting them out of your head, where they can turn round and round in a muddle, and seeing them more clearly written down takes away a bit of the pressure you feel when something's worrying you. It may also help you to talk to someone, when you have a better idea of how to express your feelings openly.

On the other hand, you may decide that you would rather not talk to someone you actually know, which is why the various helplines and organizations are such a good idea. You may find it easier to confide in someone who doesn't know you – even someone you don't have to confront face-to-face. Really, it's entirely up to you. The point is you do have choices and there's absolutely no need for you to think you have got to cope alone.

The last thing you want to hear when you're feeling down is someone telling you to 'cheer up', or to 'pull your socks up', which is likely to make you feel even more misunderstood. After all, if you *could* cheer up, you would, wouldn't you? On the other hand, there are ways in which you can try to help yourself –

or look after yourself – which can actually go a long way towards making you feel a bit better. When you're feeling unhappy, you often can't be bothered to make an effort to go out with friends. Sitting in your room may seem easier, but making even a small effort can sometimes have the effect of breaking the vicious circle of a down mood.

For instance, instead of making yourself go out to a party, perhaps suggest seeing a film with a friend, which gets you out but doesn't involve you having to force yourself into a lively mood. It's a compromise and could well give you a boost. Or, if you really don't want to go out, you could try asking a friend over – to talk, listen to music, or maybe even just watch TV together. Again, it's a compromise between being alone all the time and going to the other extreme of being with loads of people in a noisy environment which you may well not fancy. If you'd really prefer to be alone, then try to be kind to yourself. It sounds silly doesn't it, being kind to yourself. Isn't that something other people are supposed to do? Actually, the first person who needs to do that is *you*. Show yourself the love and considerationd that you want and respect from others – and tell yourself that you deserve it. Staying in on your own will feel better if you have a good book or magazine to read, relax in a bath with loads of bubbles and your favourite music to listen to, or maybe even write a letter to someone you want to keep in touch with. It doesn't matter what it is, as long as you try to think of it as your time to *allow* yourself the space you need to start feeling better.

It's important for you to acknowledge feeling sad, whatever the reason. It's also a question of knowing how you feel, allowing yourself to express your emotions and finding *positive* ways of dealing with them, apart from punishing yourself by not eating. Never ever think your feelings and moods aren't important enough to bother with.

If something is worrying or upsetting you in any way, it matters, and there are people out there who can offer you help and support. But the first person who has to care is you . . . enough to reach out for this help.

Contacts for help

- *Samaritans*
  Number in telephone directory. 24-hour confidential helpline. Non-judgemental, sympathetic towards young people, and willing to listen. It is sometimes possible to arrange to talk to a counsellor face-to-face.
- *Careline*
  0181–514 1177
  Confidential helpline for all young people with emotional/family problems.
- *Childline*
  0800–1111 Free
  24-hour helpline. All calls treated in complete confidence. Support, advice and help. This helpline is always very busy, but keep trying if you don't immediately get through. If you persevere, you will eventually get a free line. There is no charge for calls to this number.
- *NAYPCAS* (National Association of Young People's Counselling and Advisory Service)
  Send an s.a.e. to 17–23 Albion Street, Leicester LE1 6GD. They will give you details of your nearest youth counselling and advisory service. Free and confidential.

Recommended books

- Miriam Stoppard, *Every Girl's Life Guide* (Dorling Kindersley)
  Deals with lots of different aspects of growing up.
- Dorothy Rowe, *Depression: The Way Out of Your Prison* (Routledge and Kegan Paul)
  Helps you and your parents to recognize what's happening as you begin to gain weight after anorexia – and helps you to cope!
- Carol Weston, *Girltalk* (Pan Horizons)
  All the things your sister never told you. Includes a good section on school, exams, studying and how to get extra help, learn how to relax and cope generally.
- Michele Brown, *How to Study Successfully* (Sheldon)
  Advice to anyone who needs extra confidence.

12

Relationships with boys

Lots of people have written to me because they are worried about finding a boyfriend. And once you've found one, you may then have become worried about whether or not you'll get 'dumped', or whether he'll end up fancying your best friend. In a way, I think this has a lot to do with what we've talked about in the chapter about self-confidence. I've received letters from girls who've been treated so badly by boys, it's hard to believe it's really happened. But I know only too well that it has and, again, it comes down to valuing yourself enough to know that nobody should ever be given the chance to treat you badly, in *any* way. If you feel you deserve to be treated well, you simply won't accept it if someone messes you around by, say, two-timing, or letting you down in other ways. Remember, there are many different ways in which someone can mistreat you. It can be in a physical way – or it can be emotional unkindness. Whichever it is, by allowing someone to continue you're basically giving them the go-ahead to carry on behaving in this way. Changing your values – about yourself and what you feel you need and deserve – will help to change the way you expect and deserve to be treated in a relationship.

So, you look across the classroom, disco, or wherever and notice the best looking lad you've ever seen in your life. Or you may begin to notice your brother's best friend – and you think he may be staring a lot at you when you're busy looking the other way. Your best friend has heard that 'he' really likes you, but weeks pass by and neither of us has plucked up the courage to say something!

So, you carry on wondering . . . hoping . . . dreaming . . . and basically not knowing.

Personally, I don't think that passing messages backwards and forward via other friends is a very good idea, even though it seems to be quite a popular way of communicating. But, frankly, I don't think it really works. Second-hand info. can turn into wrong messages or misunderstandings and then the whole thing can become very embarrassing. So, generally, I feel that if you want to convey something to a boy, or find something out, it's usually best to do it yourself, even if it means writing a short note and giving it to the boy in question. Remember, if he's worth bothering about, he won't make fun of you or think you're being stupid for making a move.

Many girls worry about not having a boyfriend, especially if all your friends seem to be going out with someone. I know how it feels when everyone you know has got a boyfriend and you're the 'odd one out'. Apart from anything else, it makes it hard for you to acknowledge – and accept – that it's absolutely fine for you *not* to have one. Some girls seem to be more into the *idea* of having a boyfriend, and any boy will do! But will he? Again, it comes down to self-esteem, because surely it's better to wait until you meet someone you like and feel comfortable with than say yes to going out with the first creep who asks, just so that you can say you've got a boyfriend?

The main thing is to try very hard to be happy independently, because this will help you to get rid of those desperate feelings to have a boyfriend. Make the most of your friends of both sexes and try to stop worrying about whether or not your other friends are going out with someone. Even if they are and you're not, don't imagine that everything's great all the time with their boyfriends. The reality is more likely to be that there are 'ups and downs'. Whether you've got a regular boyfriend or not, being in a relationship doesn't equal 24-hours-a-day guaranteed happiness, any more than relationships with friends or family can guarantee the same.

I've received letters from girls who are so lonely without a boyfriend that they decide to stop eating properly and become anorexic.

> All my friends seem to have boyfriends and I feel completely left out, as if I'm weird or something. I've never had a boyfriend, although people say I'm quite pretty with a good personality. I really hate my thighs though and think I'm completely gross sometimes. Sometimes I stop eating properly thinking that if I can lose some weight, boys will find me

> more attractive. The trouble is, after I've starved myself for days I end up having a massive binge and then I just feel even worse . . .
>
> Karen (15), Kent

Think about this very carefully and about what is actually going on.

You don't have a boyfriend, so maybe you feel there's a sense of emptiness you can't handle on your own. This empty feeling perhaps makes you feel there must be something wrong with you. After all, you may reason, if there *wasn't* you'd have a boyfriend. You become more and more convinced that it's because of your nose, or the fact that you're not quite pretty enough . . . or too fat. So you start cutting down on food or skipping meals. You think this will somehow make you feel better, that magically the problem will resolve itself, or just go away, if you stop eating. *It won't!* What you are doing, in fact, is punishing yourself for something you haven't done and are not 'guilty' of. You're saying, I'm not worth anything without a boyfriend, so I may as well make myself hurt even more by this form of self-abuse. Can you see how very destructive this way of thinking is? How can it possibly be the case that you're not worth caring about as an individual? Remember, you are a special person in your own right. Having a boyfriend can be great. It can be fun, exciting and wonderful if he's the right boy. But the important thing to acknowledge is that having a boyfriend doesn't suddenly make you into a person of worth. You are that already – without a boyfriend.

If you can gradually start to think this way, you will improve things for yourself no end. Your self-confidence will get better and you will stop worrying so much about finding a boyfriend. Also, once you stop consciously searching for a boyfriend, chances are you may meet someone you like – and who likes you. That's the way things tend to go, so try to see the funny side of it.

If you've currently got a boyfriend, or have a good friend of the opposite sex, it's important that you feel comfortable with that person and can trust them – both with your feelings and to be trustworthy in other ways too. Plenty of girls complain that their boyfriends are very loving when it's just the two of them, but as soon as he gets with a crowd of his mates he turns into being 'cool' and macho and won't show his feelings at all. This is very hurtful immature behaviour. Quite honestly I think it happens not because the boy doesn't care, but mostly because boys too often feel under pressure to act a certain way. Try to explain to your boyfriend how you feel, and maybe if you're brave enough to say that you know what it's like when you're with a group of mates and have to live up to their expectations of you. As long as he's not being downright rude and not trying to put you down, a certain amount of his not being able to show his feelings to you in front of his friends is something you can maybe try to accept and not take personally. Again, it's a question of setting limits, knowing what is and isn't acceptable to you, and being able to talk about this together with your boyfriend.

There should be give and take in all relationships and it's important that you don't push your needs away all the time just to please your boyfriend. If he cares it will important to him to listen to you and to find out what those needs are. First you have to know for *yourself* – and that means liking and valuing who you are.

Recommended book

- Rosemary Stones, *There's More to Life Than Mr Right* (Lions Tracks)

13

Can't get over losing him: breaking up and coping

Nobody can deny that rejection hurts. If your boyfriend tells you it's over, you will inevitably feel a whole rang of emotions, which can be very difficult to cope with, especially if you don't understand what's gone wrong or why he doesn't want to go out with you any more. From this point of view, I think it's always worth asking for some kind of explanation because this will seem better than having sleepless nights worrying about where *you've* gone wrong or what's so awful about you that you've been dumped. The point is, rejection doesn't mean there's something wrong with you, it means that your boyfriend's feelings have somehow changed, and that can be for a whole lot of different reasons, some of which may not even be directly related to you. Many boys find the idea of 'going steady' quite difficult – either because of pressure from friends, or because they feel they're just not ready for such a commitment. So, does this mean there's something wrong with you?

First of all, it's important to acknowledge your feelings and allow yourself to be upset, sad, disappointed, and maybe even angry. That's OK – you're entitled to be all of these things and any other emotions which come up. Try to confide in someone, because an adult especially will in all probability be able to reassure you that they too have been through something similar and you do get over it.

Try to indulge yourself a bit by treating yourself to nice warm baths, early nights with some magazines or a book to read. Try to go out with a friend, or ask her to spend some time with you. Try to take care of your health around this time because it's tempting to start neglecting yourself when a relationship breaks up. Maybe you feel you're just not 'worth it' and you stop eating properly because you're just not able to tell someone just how sad you feel? As I've said, it's important to try to share these feelings and even more important to acknowledge them for yourself. It's rather like grieving. You need to feel and to go through what's happening, then you will feel stronger and much more able to go cope and go forward.

Some girls feel that finding another boyfriend straight away will take away the hurt. Well, to some extent that's true, but you've probably heard of the expression 'on the rebound'. Going out with someone new before you've given yourself a chance to come to terms with what's happened and get over what's happened, can mean that all those different feelings will just be pushed underneath. You need to acknowledge and express them, and to give yourself some time and space to recover. Then you will be ready to start a new relationship. Your experience will have helped you to be more aware and hopefully even more independent, so that a break-up of a relationship won't seem like the end of the world.

Many people ask whether staying friends is a good idea. I don't think there is a set answer to this – each situation is different and although it may feel right for you to stay on friendly terms with your ex-boyfriend, it may not be a good idea for someone else. In any case, I feel you need time before you can become 'just friends'. It's difficult suddenly to accept an ex as being someone you see as a friend but not a boyfriend, especially if you didn't want the relationship to end. Time will tell whether or not a friendship will be possible, or even what you really want. Try not to hold on by saying you want to be friends, when really what you mean is you can't accept parting. Accepting the separation will ultimately help you to meet again as friends, if that's what you both want.

Finally, when you break up you may well feel that you don't want anybody else if you can't go out with 'him'. Or you may think you won't ever find anyone else. It feels that way, but I promise you things *will* change and get better. 'Time heals' is another one of those sayings that people expect you to understand, when all you know is that you'll *never* get over it! Although I realize that you need to experience it yourself before you're ever going to believe it's possible, I can only be another one of those people who can assure you 'time heals'!

Contacts for help

- *Careline*
  0181–514 1177
  Helpline for all young people with problems.
- *Samaritans*
  Listed in your local telephone directory. 24-hour confidential helpline.

Recommended book

- Anne Dickson, *A Woman In Your Own Right* (Quartet)
  Clearly written and informative. Looks at ways in which you can become more assertive and express anger.

14

Should I say Yes to having sex

Firstly, there seems little point in pretending that girls under sixteen don't have sex. I know this isn't the case, but at the same time I think it's important to think about what the legal age of consent means to you if you're not yet sixteen. Basically, this law, which says it is illegal for a boy/man to have sex with a girl who's below the age of sixteen, exists to help protect you. Having sex involves adopting a real sense of responsibility towards yourself and the other person. This responsibility involves caring about your physical and emotional health and well-being.

For instance, if you are fifteen and in a steady relationship, you may reach a stage where you feel you are ready to have a sexual relationship. Doing so without protection means that you not only risk unwanted pregnancy, you would also be increasing your risk of getting a sexually transmitted infection, including the HIV virus which can lead to AIDS. On the emotional side, starting a sexual relationship will mean that you will become more involved, feel more vulnerable and, therefore, more easily hurt. Try to make a decision about sex from a well thought out viewpoint, taking care to be clued-up about protecting yourself and the risks involved. You may not think this sounds very romantic but judging by the hundreds of letters I've received from girls who've taken unnecessary risks, the fear of unwanted pregnancy, rejection – and often regret and embarrassment – don't add up to paint a very romantic picture. In actual fact, it's far more satisfying to know that you've made a decision which is right for you and one which isn't likely to cause you distress afterwards.

My advice would be to try to make sure that the relationship is going reasonably well and that you've been together for more than just a few days, or even a few weeks, which definitely isn't long enough really to get to know someone properly and build up some trust and friendship between you. At the end of the day, if and when you have sex is a decision only you can make. But at least let it be *your* decision, one that you've thought through.

Many girls say that they've been in some way pressurized into having sex. You've said that he'll stop going out with you if you say no, or that he'll call you 'tight' or 'frigid' if you don't agree to sex. Remember, it matters that you have respect for your own body. Nobody has the right to have sex with you – it's your choice. No way should you ever allow yourself to be blackmailed into it. Try to see it in this light, this is what it amounts to if your boyfriend calls you names or threatens to reject you just because you won't sleep with him. If he cares about you, likes and respects you, he will accept your decision if you say the time isn't right for you, for whatever reason. This applies whether or not you are underage. Reaching the age of sixteen doesn't mean you automatically have to agree to having sex. It may be a while before it feels right for you – it may not. Set up some values for yourself. It matters not a jot whether your best mate is sleeping with her boyfriend, or whether half your class regularly has sex. How do you know it's really true, anyway?

There also seems to be quite a lot of pressure from other girls who may call you a 'slag' if you *do* sleep with a boy, or something just as bad if you *don't.* While I very much sympathize with how distressing it can be to get labelled with names like this, it may help to think about how meaningless they are when often it's just referring to a girl who simply may not have a steady boyfriend. Try to get this into perspective. Are you going to allow other people to take away your right to be single, in the sense that you're not going steady? And if you don't agree to having sex, how on earth can that justify being called another abusive name as if there's something wrong with you? There isn't.

Being indiscriminate or 'easy' about boys you sleep with is something I hope you yourself will realize is a dangerous path for you to follow. Don't allow name-calling to be your yardstick for how you should behave. Sleeping around won't do anything for your self-esteem, or for your health, nor is it likely to lead you into a satisfying relationship with a boy. Being without a boyfriend, or having more than one boy as a close friend doesn't mean you are 'easy' – it means you are exercising your right to choose not to be in a steady relationship.

A very casual approach to sex won't ultimately make you feel good about yourself, as many of the letters I receive confirm. I know it can be difficult for you if you feel you have to 'compete'. But how you approach sex from the very start will help to form a lot of the feelings you have – about yourself and your relationships with boys in the future. Sex can be something very special between two people who care about each other, or it can be a way in which you allow yourself to be used or use others.

Becoming sexually aware can produce all kinds of new feelings which may seem exciting, overwhelming, perhaps even frightening. It takes time for these feelings to develop and for you to become aware of your needs and emotions within a sexual relationship. Decide what's right for you, and always make sure that if you are ready you will be safe not very sorry.

Many girls write because they are confused about their feelings of sexuality. A question I've often been asked is: 'I fancy another girl – do you think I'm a lesbian?' The question may come from a girl of maybe thirteen or fourteen, or maybe older. As I've said, when you're becoming sexually aware it is quite natural to have a mixture of feelings and some of these may well involve an attraction to the same sex. There's nothing at all wrong with that. In fact, I would suspect any adult of not being totally honest if they said they'd never ever experienced these feelings when the were growing up. Personally, I don't feel you need to make any big decisions about this when you are in your very early teens. Give your feelings time to develop and settle down because your attraction, or attractions, to the same sex will in all probability prove to be a passing phase.

But, being a lesbian or gay is OK. Each and every one of us has the right to choose how we express our sexuality and if these feelings develop in time and you want to explore them, this is a choice you should be allowed to make. In this situation I always feel it helps to talk to people who are involved in helping young people to sort out these feelings. Whether you know you are gay, think you might be or are worried about any aspect of this, there are organizations which can talk things over with you and also put you in touch with other young gay people for support and social contact.

Many girls have doubts and fears about their bodies or are unsure about the facts of life. It makes sense to be clued-up about every aspect of periods, contraception, how you can and can't get pregnant – *before* you have sex. Not knowing just increases your sense of having no control over what happens to you. Remember, you do have control – and you also have choices!

Contacts for help

- *Brooks Advisory Centres*
  Central Office, 153a East Street, London SE17 2SD.
  Tel. 0171–708 1234 for your nearest Centre. Brook Centres are in eight cities throughout the country. They offer free confidential advice and counselling on contraception, pregnancy testing unplanned pregnancy, infection testing or referral, and abortion referral. Brook Centres are friendly, sympathetic and non-judgemental. Their aim is to provide information and support to help young people make decisions, without any pressure or being told what to do. Girls and boys are welcome, either together or separately. Some very helpful publications are also available. Brook also runs a national 24-hour confidential helpline on 0171–410 0420, offering advice on contraception, pregnancy, abortion and sexually transmitted diseases.
- *Family Planning Association Clinics* (FPA)
  27–35 Mortimer Street, London W1N 7RJ. Tel. 0171–636 7866 for your nearest clinic. Free personal and confidential advice (11 a.m.–3 p.m. weekdays) on up-to-date information about contraception, sexuality, periods, etc.
- *London Friend*
  86 Caledonian Road, Kings Cross, London N1 9DN.
  Tel. 0171–837 3337, 7.30 p.m.–10 p.m.
  Free confidential, befriending and counselling for people worried about their sexuality.

Recommended books

- Jane Cousins Mills, *Make it Happy, Make it Safe* (Penguin)
  Sympathetic direct information and advice about safe sex and taking responsibility for your emotional and physical well-being.

- Kaye Wellings, *First Love First Sex – A Practical Guide to Relationships* (Thorsons)
  Lots of information about coping with intimate relationships. A straightforward, helpful and sympathetic guide.

15

Sexual abuse

I realize it's taken a lot of courage and honesty for people to write telling me about their experiences of some form of abuse. It can't be easy and my heart goes out to the many girls who have been brave enough to put their thoughts on paper and share their experiences with me.

I've always been struck by the huge sense of guilt which seems to go hand in hand with these experiences. It is so very important for you to acknowledge that if you have been abused, whether it's by a stranger or someone you know well and have trusted, *you are never to blame.* An adult is always responsible if a child has been abused, and this applies even if you went along with what happened because you were afraid to say 'No.' It doesn't matter one bit whether or not you allowed the abuse to continue over a period of time, especially if the abuse has taken place within the family. Remember, you put your trust in someone who is supposed to care for you and protect you, and abuse is a betrayal of that trust.

Many people who have written to me about their experience of abuse feel so ashamed and upset that they turn these emotions inwards and stop eating. It's very important that you not only realize that you don't deserve to be punished, but also that you deserve to be given help and support too – not further hurt. Instead of directing your very understandable confused and painful feelings back towards yourself by not eating, or trying to harm yourself in another way, it's very necessary that you find ways of expressing them openly, to someone who will understand, be sympathetic and give you all the help you need.

Supposing the abuse took place some time ago when you were much younger and you've never told anybody and still feel very guilty about it. Perhaps you imagine that because it's in the past and nobody knows, you somehow have no right to talk about it. You may try to push all your thoughts about what happened to the back of your mind, but there are feelings and emotions you just can't seem to deal with on your own.

Sometimes what happens is that girls who've been abused have written to me when they begin a sexual relationship with a boy they really like, but then find they can't bear their boyfriend to touch them or to go anywhere near them. If this has been your experience, I can imagine that this has made you feel even more guilty. After all, you really care about this boy, you just don't want him close to you. What on earth can be wrong with me, you may be asking. Girls in this situation have told me that their relationships have sometimes broken up, because either the boy can't understand what's happening, or the feelings of guilt and disgust are so great that the girl herself ends the relationship to escape the difficult feelings.

In the same way that not eating doesn't help you to resolve this kind of situation, neither does turning your back on the feelings and walking away from them. In fact, becoming anorexic is doing just that, except it gives you yet another problem to deal with along the way.

I've sensed an enormous amount of anger, hurt and shame in the letters about abuse and it saddens me a lot to realize that so much of this anger, and the other emotions, are not being allowed to come out in a constructive way. Anorexia – and other self-destructive actions – may seem to take the pain away . . . temporarily. But these drastic measures can never be the safe answer for you.

If you have been abused it doesn't mean that you don't deserve to be loved and it doesn't mean that you deserve to suffer any more. You don't. On the other hand, whatever strong emotions you are experiencing – whether it's hate, sadness, disgust, shame – these are all natural, normal reactions to the kind of experience you've had. They don't mean you're a bad person, just a very human and sensitive one with feelings which can be hurt and need to be mended. It matters that you find the courage to reach out for the help available to you. I believe that before you are given the opportunity to come to terms with what has happened, it can be very difficult for you to put your trust in someone of the opposite sex. In a sense, you need the time and opportunity to allow that trust to develop by first coming to terms with what has happened. Again, this is nothing at all to be ashamed or embarrassed about. There's no 'ought to' where forming relationships is concerned after abuse. Of course, you will at some point no doubt *want* to – but that is a very different thing and can and will happen when the time is right for *you.*

Some girls have told me that the very act of meeting a boy they really like and who is understanding, patient, and kind can help to overcome all the hurt of the past. Sometimes the boy himself gives enough support to make talking to an experienced counsellor possible, and when that happens it must be very, very encouraging. But if you haven't got such a boyfriend, what's much more important, is that you give yourself the chance to approach someone who can help you.

The first step is often the hardest and that's why even writing a letter can be difficult. However, people have often said that the simple act of writing things down can begin to make a difference. Maybe it would help you to begin by writing down how you feel – perhaps in a diary, not necessarily to show anyone else. The next stage is to contact someone you know you can trust to listen and understand, as well as giving you all the help and support you need. Remember, there are special counselling helplines which exist to help people like you talk about abuse, so that help can be offered. There is never any question of being judged or blamed, only ever the desire to protect and support you, so you needn't be afraid to reach out for this help.

You may have tried the anorexic way, and you know deep in your heart that it can never be the answer. There is another way to cope with abuse, a much safer, better way which will help you to come to terms with what has happened. Then you will be able gradually to put your experience in the past where it belongs.

Contacts for help

- *Samaritans*
  Listed in your local telephone directory, or call the operator.
- *Childline*
  0800–1111 FREE
  If you can't get through the first time, keep trying. You will eventually get a line if you persevere.
  Both the Samaritans and Childline operate a 24-hour totally confidential sympathetic helpline.

- *Careline*
  0181–514 1177
  A sympathetic, confidential helpline for all young people.
- *Janine Turner – Abuse therapist*
  01793–731286
  Receives hundreds of calls from girls who've been abused. She will understand what you've been through and will be able to help you.

Recommended books

- Ouaine Bain and Maureen Sanders, *Out in the Open: A Guide for Young People Who Have Been Abused* (Virago Upstart)
- Rosemary Stones, *Too Close Encounters and What To Do About Them* (Piccadilly Press)
  How to keep yourself safe and what to do if you find yourself in a difficult/uncomfortable situation.
- Hadley Irwin, *A Girl Like Abby* (Plus Fiction)
  Fiction – talking about sexual abuse and coping with the experience.

16

Families

There's a saying which goes 'You can choose your friends but not your family' . . . And yet, family ties seem to bring up the strongest of emotions and however many arguments take place the need to be with your family and to receive their love and acceptance is usually a very important issue for many young people.

The process of becoming a separate person can seem complicated. There may be times when you want to be totally independent and resent your parent's intrusion into your 'territory'. There will be other times when you want to feel safe and for things to be the way they've always been, like when you were much younger. That feeling may throw you, because you might imagine you have to be one thing or another. A coping and independent adult, or vulnerable child. You don't! It's perfectly natural to experience this mixture of feelings; even adults don't feel grown up all the time.

But, rather than trying to force yourself to be something you're not and generally giving yourself a hard time over these conflicting feelings, try to talk to your parents about it. I used to think parents couldn't understand anything like that, but remember they were your age once and it won't be impossible for them in some way to relate to these feelings. As I've said, even grown ups can have them. I remember my parents once saying to me 'We weren't born at the age of forty . . . we do understand'! It seems funny now, but at the same time I guess I did believe that they'd never been in their teens. So try to give your parents a chance to understand you.

Often it seems you are just not able to confide in one or both of your parents, even though you may desperately want to share a problem with someone who will care about your feelings. I remember once receiving a letter from a young girl's mother which explained how she wanted to ask all young girls to try to approach their mums with a problem, because she hadn't realized how unhappy her daughter had been until she encouraged her to confide in her. I realize that not everyone is able to do this with a parent, but I do think it's important to consider them as your first possibility, at least, when it comes to sharing a worry – or any problem you'r experiencing. Many people say 'They'll never understand' or 'They'll kill me if they find out . . .' Often, however, the fear of approaching your mum and dad is often worse than actually doing it. And remember, parents don't always react in the way you imagine they will. When it comes to the crunch most parents want to offer their children the best they can with love and support. Sometimes, though, it takes a bit of extra help from *you* in approaching them for this support.

If you approach your parents/guardians and they don't respond in the way you hope or expect, please don't give up. *It doesn't mean you've done something wrong.* Sometimes parents/guardians may be unable to cope with the situation themselves, and could have strong feelings of their own, such as anger, frustration – maybe guilt – or even denial that there *is* a problem. Again, I emphasise, this isn't your fault. You haven't made a mistake by approaching them – you've taken a brave step. It's quite possible that given time, they *will* feel able to give you the support you need. But, if not, believe that it's still worth seeking help and support for yourself. There are plenty of suggestions in the section at the end of the book, called 'How to find help', on page 108.

Family relationships can be complicated and it may make you feel very guilty to realize that you don't always have loving feelings for your parents, brothers or sisters. Or sometimes you may feel a lot of love, while at other times you experience the very opposite . . . hatred. Then, there may be times when you feel much closer to one parent than the other, and then again, as if to throw you even more, the whole thing changes round. Try hard to acknowledge that in most families there are times when there is a mixture of these feelings. It doesn't mean you're a bad person or are guilty of anything terrible. No family is perfect and thinking such a family exists is a myth. Don't try to deny the feelings you have – it's much better for you to acknowledge them even if they're not easy ones to accept.

If you fight with your sister or brother or feel you're being unfairly treated in some way, try very hard to discuss it with your parents rather than allow it to get out of hand. There's a big difference between yelling 'You always favour her and don't let me do anything I want' and sitting down calmly with your mum and dad – and maybe your sister – and explaining that you get upset if your sister is allowed to get away with things you seem to get punished for. This is just an example, but I tend to think if you try to approach things in a sensible way you are more likely to get a sensible response!

What if you can't talk to your parents about whatever's bothering you? Again, there are people who can help and support you in complete confidence, so there's absolutely no need to isolate yourself with a problem, however small or big it seems to be. If it's bothering you, it's worth finding someone who can listen, advise, help and support you.

If there are problems in your family, or your parents have separated, never feel you are to blame for this happening. It may be very difficult indeed for you to accept your parents' breaking up, and some young people seem to feel responsible and torn between their two parents. Nobody could deny this is hard to cope with, but try to understand that adults rarely make this decision lightly and it doesn't mean that either of your parents doesn't love you or is rejecting you.

Talking to a helpline counsellor on the phone, or finding a special youth counselling agency where you can talk things over with someone face-to-face, isn't being weak or stupid. Often it can be easier to talk to someone who's not directly involved with your problems because, as well as being able to give you their professional support, an 'outsider' can be more objective about your situation. You may find that once you've started to confide in someone like this, it then becomes easier to share your problem with your parents or guardian, or perhaps a close relative or friend.

You may have become anorexic in an attempt to cope with certain family conflicts, or even just feelings at home that you can't really put your finger on but are causing you distress. Naturally, your parents are going to start asking questions and become concerned and worried about you. They may even become angry and try to pressurize you into eating, which I understand will make you feel even more upset. I know this will be a very difficult time for you. On the one hand you desperately want them to care, while on the other you don't want them to interfere or stop you from not eating which seems to you to be the only way of dealing with how you feel. I do understand how very hard this kind of situation is to face because I have experienced something similar. Although I cannot possibly say my feelings were the same as yours, because everybody is an individual. I believe I can identify with this kind of situation.

Obviously, your parents don't understand *why* you're not eating and your mum especially may get very upset about it, which just makes you feel more guilty and yet more determined to carry on. Maybe you can see that saying 'no' to food could be your way of trying to express your feelings . . . of anger, resentment, sadness and the need to be a special person. It doesn't help if you feel you have to measure up to expectations or compete with someone else in the family. Remember, often you are the one striving to be perfect, when other people in the family would be happy to accept you for youreslf. There's really no such thing as perfection when it comes to people. Being vulnerable in certain ways, or simply just not as good at some things as other things, isn't a fault. It just means you're human!

The important thing in families – as with any other kinds of relationships – is communication. The important thing for you is expressing your feelings in a way which isn't going to harm you, such as not eating. I hope you are gradually beginning to acknowledge that starving is a form of expressing all kinds of feelings – but a very destructive and harmful way indeed.

Maybe your mum and dad try to tempt you with food, or think of eating as a shared family occasion which you fear and dread if you have become anorexic. So what often happens is that mealtimes become a battleground and all you seem to be doing is arguing about what you have and haven't eaten. You may become secretive and lie about the huge lunch you've eaten at school, when in fact youve had very little or nothing. You can see how the whole issue revolves around food at home, when really this isn't what it's all about.

This is why it is so very important for you to try hard to accept that something's wrong, that your way of coping won't make things better for you, and that you need to confront these feelings by finding someone who can understand and who will listen and give you the help you need. If you've tried to talk to your parents but just can't at the moment, remember there are specially trained counsellors to turn to. You may feel your problems are just too close to home, or you just can't yet confide in your parents that something's wrong. Of course, this can only happen when you yourself recognize this, but try as hard as you can to accept that if your family nag, even shout or plead with you to eat, it's not because they want you to get fat, but because they really care about you and want you to get better. They may also feel confused and guilty about what's happening. In a way, they may need some help too, so that they can understand.

Contacts for help

- *NAYPCAS*
  17–23 Albion Street, Leicester LE1 6GD.
  For details of your nearest youth counselling advisory service. Free and confidential.
- *Careline*
  0181–514 1177
  Confidential helpline for all young people.
- *Samaritans*
  Listed in your local telephone directory.
  24-hour confidential helpline. Non-judgemental and sympathetic towards young people.

Recommended books

- Dr David Bennet, *Growing Pains* (Thorsons)
  Covers all issues that parents and young people experience in a non-heavy way. Written for young people and parents with the aim to help both to communicate better.
- Sue Sharpe, *Voices from Home: Girls Talk About Their Families* (Virago Upstarts)
- Jane Dowdeswell, *Sisters On Sisters* (Thorsons)
  Sisters talk about each other and their relationships, including feelings like affection, envy, frustration, and friendship.
- Judy Blume, *It's Not the End of the World* (Piper)
  About coping with divorce.
- Jill Krementz, *How It Feels When Parents Divorce* (Gollancz)

Children of varying ages discuss their parents' divorce and what it meant to them.

Both these last two books offer understanding and hope for the future.

17

Am I normal?

This is something many young people ask because when you are growing up feelings about your looks, how others see you and whether or not you are 'normal' and acceptable are usually very intense. You quite probably think you're too fat, too tall, too short, not pretty enough, too freckly or just downright plain. Whatever you happen to think is wrong with you let me assure you that you do have good points, whether you can believe it at the moment or not, and it's far better to think about these rather than dwelling on what you see as an imperfection. The idea of perfection, in any case, is an imaginary one. Even the most beautiful people can find fault with themselves. The point is you don't have to conform to an impossible ideal in order to look and feel attractive. Everyone is different. *So what* if a particular boy you like isn't keen on your bright red hair. Someone else will love it – and you should too. In fact, accepting the parts of yourself you can't realistically change and making the best of whatever's left is one of the most important ways of feeling good about yourself. When you do, other people will respond in a much more positive way to you than if you're constantly putting yourself down. *Feeling confident means first accepting and liking yourself.*

To a certain extent what you wear – even the colours – can make a statement about you, but it's easy to focus on a part of your body you don't like and blame everything that goes wrong on that.

It's just possible that a change of attitude towards yourself will actually make a lot of difference to how you feel. I think most young people want their parents – their mothers in particular – to make them feel good about themselves by telling them how great they look. Unfortunately this doesn't always happen and you may not get the affirmation you want. You may even feel criticized. You obviously want to know that you are good enough, but sometimes your parents might give you mixed messages about this. This may be because they find it quite difficult to say what you want to hear for their own reasons which actually have nothing to do with you. If you don't get this affirmation, you have to find a way of giving it to yourself. You have to develop your own self-esteem and gradually build self-confidence by accepting yourself and the fact that you are an individual with lots of offer.

While you are growing up and developing, you may want to know whether your breasts are the 'right' size, your sexual organs the shape and size they 'should' be. The fact is that each and every one of us develops at our own pace and there's no point in worrying that if your breasts are smaller or bigger than your best mate's then it means you've got a problem. You haven't! And, believe me, for every letter I've received from a girl, who's concerned about her breasts being too small. I've received another from someone worried because she thinks her breasts are too big. What's important is that you try to accept yourself, instead of comparing yourself unfavourably with others.

For instance, it's perfectly normal to have one breast bigger than the other, basically because the two sides of our bodies are not exactly the same. Even the two sides of our faces aren't identical – hence people sometimes asking to be photographed on their 'best' side. I've received many letters from girls who are worried because their nipples turn in instead of sticking out (known as 'inverted' nipples). I hope I can reassure you by saying that lots of girls and women have inverted nipples and it's nothing to worry about. Sometimes, as your breasts continue to develop the nipples will be pushed out, but if this doesn't happen there's absolutely no need for concern. It won't stop you from enjoying sex, or from breast-feeding a baby should you wish to in the future, since there are special breast shields available to help women with inverted nipples who want to breast-feed. *It helps to understand your body and not to be afraid of it.*

If you are seriously worried about any aspect of your body, even if it's in a place you feel embarrassed about, always check this out with your doctor. Even if you know you'll feel awkward for a few minutes, surely this is far better than weeks or months spent worrying over something your doctor can reassure you about. I know from the letters I've received that many people find this very difficult. But try to remember that doctors see many patients every day and are completely used to being asked all kinds of questions. They're not embarrassed and don't feel awkward – it's part of their job and you will invariably find doctors are very matter-of-fact about something you imagine is a huge embarrassment. However small or unimportant you think the problem may be don't think you'll be wasting a doctor's time if you need advice and reassurance. It wastes far more time if you sit at home fretting about something which in all possibility will turn out to be nothing at all to worry about. Also, there may well be something positive you can do, say, to remove a mole which is *really* unsightly – it's worth asking.

You may feel quite frightened at the thought of developing a bust and becoming sexually attractive, when inside you feel you're not ready for any of that. Your periods may start and again, although you're told this is a good sign, it can also seem quite scarey. Many girls feel that just because their periods have started it means they have to change overnight and become mature adults. Nobody would expect this to happen . . . and it doesn't. It's a gradual process. The main thing to remember is that finding out all about periods will help you to feel much better about them because lack of understanding can lead to confusion about the facts and more unnecessary worries. Try to talk to your mum about periods, or even an older sister if you've got one. They've experienced periods and will be able to understand what's happening, reassure you and give you advice. Sometimes mums are a bit reluctant to approach the subject because they may sense your embarrassment, or even feel a bit embarrassed themselves. But if you ask direct questions and explain that you want to have a chat about things it will be much easier for you both.

If you are anorexic, your periods will probably stop, or they may be delayed in arriving if you haven't yet started. If you starve yourself, your breast development will suffer. Maybe the thought of these developments and changes are concerning you so much that you feel the answer is not to eat because then you will stay just the way you are, which may feel safer.

Instead of giving you the control you want in putting these things 'on hold', not eating will give you the much bigger problem of coping with the effects of anorexia. It is far, far better to confront these fears, doubts and worries you have about growing up. They are normal feelings and by finding the courage to express them you will discover other ways of coping.

Many of you have worries about crushes on teachers, pop singers, actors and so on. These feelings are valid – not ones you need to force yourself to get over quickly, or feel ashamed of. They don't mean you're 'weird'. Very often, having these crushes when you're very young is a way of testing out your emotions in preparation for the time when you will form relationships with boys. There's nothing wrong with having a crush on someone of your own sex – it doesn't mean there's something wrong with you. It often happens at a time when you are exploring your sexual feelings, or even looking to a female who may be older than you as someone you can look up to and perhaps be influenced by. Again, this is perfectly OK.

But if a crush starts to take up all your waking time and you can't concentrate or think about anything else – and don't even want to form other relationships, in case you spoil your chances with *him* or *her* – then things have obviously got out of hand. Try to talk things through with someone you trust, so that you can get things into perspective. Acknowledge you have these strong feelings, but also try to get yourself involved in other things too. It may seem very painful and difficult for you, but eventually you will be able to see all this in a different light.

What about body hair? Everyone has a certain amount of facial/body hair. Earlier in the book I explained that anorexics often develop an increase in general body hair. The medical term used to describe it is *lanugo*. It is thought to be a biological response to starvation. However, as with other side-effects of anorexia, when you recover and are eating normally, this fine body hair will stop appearing. Generally speaking, some girls have more facial/body hair than others and this applies to healthy, non-anorexic girls. It so happens that in our society, girls and women prefer to remove what's called 'superfluous' hair, or 'unwanted' hair. But, this doesn't mean you're not normal if you choose not to get rid of it. However, if you feel you have really excessive body hair which seems far too much to try removing yourself, go to your doctor, because in some unusual cases this may be due to a hormonal imbalance which can be corrected. Or it may be possible to have electrolysis on the NHS. It's not a question of 'normality': it's a question of balance and sometimes this balance is upset. Depilatories (hair removers), hair waxes, bleaching and (for under-arms and legs only) shaving, are all good ways of dealing with unwanted hair. As yet, the only permanent method of hair removal is electrolysis, but it can be a lengthy and expensive business. It's essential to have this done at a registered beauty salon, and you should always have an initial consultation to find out how long it will take and how much it will cost. Again, though, remember that you may develop an increase in general body hair (lanugo) because you've become anorexic.

When it comes to your height, the shape of your legs, or the colour of your skin, there are some things we all have to learn to accept about ourselves because we can't change them. For every person who writes to me because they are unhappy about being 'too tall' there will be an equal number of people writing because they describe themselves as 'midgets'. In other words, you want what somebody else has got, but they want what you've got! Far better to accept who and what you are and set about changing things which are *realistic* to change, such as hair that becomes too dry and needs more conditioning and looking after, or bad skin which may be helped by seeing your doctor. If you constantly think that your shortness only means you can't be a model or your tallness means that you've got to slouch around trying to look shorter – you're limiting your choices and being unrealistic about acceptance of yourself.

Contacts for help

- *Careline*
  0181–514–1177
  Confidential helpline for young people.

Recommended books

- Jill Dawson, *How Do I Look?* (Virago Upstarts)
  Girls talk about how they feel about their looks and self-image.
- Ruth Bell and others, *Changing Bodies Changing Lives* (Random House)

Although I realize this is quite expensive for some young people, it's a book well worth investing in – full of information on relationships, birth control, emotional and physical care.

18

Best friends or worst enemies?

When friendships are going well they're brilliant, but when something happens to upset that friendship it can effect how you feel quite a lot. A common problem seems to be what I call the three-way friendship. Three good friends, until one person (not always the same one) gets left out. I can remember this happening a lot when I was at school and went around with two other girls. When it was my turn to be the odd-one-out I felt pretty miserable, but for some unknown reason the situation was always changing. In this kind of situation I think it may help to remind yourself that three is a difficult number where friendships are concerned and if you do get left out I wouldn't mind betting it has nothing at all to do with anything you've done wrong. The worst thing you can do in three-way friendships is to take sides or talk behind the third friend's back to your other friend. It all gets really silly and complicated – you don't need it! If there's a problem between you, try as much as you can to sort it out between yourselves – all three of you. If you're the one who feels left out, see if you can sort it out by talking to the two other girls involved. Sometimes, just waiting for a bit without doing anything will result in them forgetting whatever it was they had got annoyed about. If it was an argument, it will often blow over if you try to avoid getting the other two girls to gang up against each other. I never think this is a good idea, neither is trying to split up two other friends so that you can form a friendship with just one of them. If the problem is to do with one particular best friend who doesn't want you to have any other friends apart from her, I think it's important to realize that friends don't own you and it's not really fair to expect you to spend all your time with just one friend without being able to see anyone else or do anything else. Try to explain to this friend that she's your best and special friend, and that you're not rejecting her by having other friends. In fact, it's likely to help you appreciate her all the more.

I realize that finding a best friend is often very important to you, though sometimes if either one of you starts going out with a boy the friendship can suffer. If it's your friend who meets a boy, recognize that the feelings you have may not necessarily all be good ones. Feeling jealous, rejected, even resentful, are natural reactions if you've spent most of your time with your friend and then suddenly things change. Try to talk this over with her. Explain how much you value your friendship and then, between you, try to work out ways in which you can get to see each other without it upsetting either her new relationship or your friendship. One doesn't have to cancel out the other – you can have both! It's important not to neglect friendships if you're the one who's just found a boyfriend. Of course, it's only natural that you'll want to see a lot of him and your conversation is bound to be all about 'him' to start with. Again, if it's this way round, discuss it with your best friend, so that she doesn't feel you're pushing her away. Remember, the situation could be reversed.

If things become difficult with friends at school and you're being picked on or bullied, then you should definitely tell an adult you can trust or call one of the helplines listed at the end of this section. Many schools are getting wise to bullying and are trying to work out ways of overcoming it, so you should never let these situations get out of hand before you tell someone. You may be worrying about why you're being bullied and think it must be your fault. You may use not eating as a way of turning your feelings back towards yourself, when really it would help you so much more to bring them out into the open. You're entitled to be afraid, to feel angry and upset. Why punish yourself even more for something you haven't done? Basically, bullies are cowards who need to pick on other people in order to boost their own self-confidence. In many ways, a bully is someone with a problem too, and needs help in confronting the way their actions not only hurt others, but are very negative for them also. Remember, whatever names you may get called, they are just that . . . pathetic names. Find some support, keep trying until you get someone to help you. Don't give up, and most of all never feel you deserve to be bullied.

Sometimes friendships can go wrong for no apparent reason. One minute everything's find and then you seem to be falling out all the time. It may be that you've been friends for a while but you're both slowly changing. It doesn't necessarily have to be the end of the friendship if you talk it over and try to find out how each of you feels about things. If your friend ultimately chooses someone else to go around with, what can you do? Again, don't be afraid to acknowledge how you feel about it happening and try to talk to someone in your family, or maybe even a close friend of the family, about what's happened. Don't bottle these feelings up or imagine you should be grown up enough to deal with it on your own. Maybe you will feel able to, but if not it's not a crime to need to share what's happened with someone you feel able to confide in.

Remember, some friendships are good, some not so good. There are ups and down in *all* relationships and even an ideal friendship won't be ideal all the time.

Contacts for help

- *Careline*
  0181–514–1177
  Confidential and sympathetic helpline for young people.
- *Childline*
  0800–1111 FREE
  24–hour confidential and sympathetic helpline. Difficult to get through but persevere and you'll get a free line eventually.

Recommended books

- Susan Albertson, *Between the Lines* (Armada)
  Fiction – about friends who realize that friendship doesn't have to end with growing up.
- J. D. Salinger, *The Catcher In the Rye* (Penguin)
  Funny yet moving account of a boy's relationships, thoughts and feelings.

19

You don't have to be perfect: learning to express anger and assert yourself

You may not believe this, but you don't have to be 'nice' all the time! Before you rush away to be rude to the first person who gets in your way, I don't mean you should make a conscious effort to be argumentative just for the sake of it. However, if you are anorexic you may well believe that in order to be accepted you have to be absolutely perfect and 'good' all the time. Anything less may make you feel anxious and upset.

The point is that as human beings none of us are perfect and anyone who expects or tries to be is setting very unrealistic goals which are bound to cause disappointment. Also, stop to think how tedious it would be to have constantly to live up to being perfect . . . never being allowed to feel or be vulnerable.

Along with this strive for perfection, you may hold back on certain feelings such as anger and speaking out for yourself, because good girls don't get angry, do they? However, feeling, acknowledging and expressing anger in a constructive, healthy way can help you release a lot of tension, as can asserting yourself by say something like, 'Actually, I don't agree with what you say' or 'My view is such-and-such . . .'

This may sound like quite a hard thing for you to do, especially if you've been used to taking a back seat and never voicing your opinion. Perhaps you're not even sure what your opinion is. Again, this is something that can happen when you get caught up in the grip of anorexia. It somehow takes away your ability to make decisions and stand up for yourself properly. Anorexia ensures that you put aside difficult feelings and even protects you from them. You learn to be very good at avoiding things like anger. But you can gradually learn to be very good at expressing feelings too! Don't think you have to be able to do this immediately. It takes time to change your habit of pushing feelings aside. Gradually it will be possible for you to put yourself first for a change.

You can make a start by trying to be open and honest with yourself and with others. You'd be amazed at how most people respond very positively to this. It's a great feeling to discover that saying what you *really* believe and asserting yourself doesn't drive people away from you. When I was anorexic. I used to think that if I got angry with someone I cared about they would reject me, so I made sure I never ever got in touch with my anger. Part of being anorexic – or hurting yourself in any way – is an expression of anger in itself, except it's directed back at *you*, rather than outwards where it belongs.

I know it may sound silly to you, but in a way you may need at first to practise getting angry, practise at speaking out. After all, if you've spent so long trying to be good all the time, you may not really know how to start feeling other things too. For instance, if something happens to upset you and your immediate reaction is to eat even less, try to understand what it is you're really feeling. That weight in your stomach as though you're about to explode, or perhaps just a general feeling of frustration or lack of motivation – what are these feelings telling you? If someone has done something which you find unacceptable (whatever it is) you may at first just feel hurt and upset, or you may even want to cry about it. This is perfectly OK. But what about also feeling angry – outraged that someone has dared to behave in this way towards you? These feelings are OK too. And when you start to acknowledge this and allow it to happen, you will begin to feel a whole lot better about yourself.

You can start by physically punching cushions (not the person you're angry with)! Believe it or not, this allows the anger to come out and won't harm anyone. You may want to begin by testing out your feelings on someone you trust and feel safe with. Tell them about your feelings so they're prepared for the change! You could also try to find out if there are any assertiveness training classes in your area (the local library will give you details), or ask your P.E. teacher if she/he can help. Assertiveness is being able to speak your mind, saying what you need and want in a direct way. Other people usually respect you if you are assertive because it also helps them to know exactly where they stand with you. It works both ways in friendships if you can learn to do this.

It may take you quite a while before you get the hang of what it means to feel angry. I'm not at all suggesting you will overnight be able to express this emotion. First, you have to feel it and acknowledge what it is.

If you have become anorexic, or harm yourself in some other way, you may believe that anger isn't anything at all to do with you and how you feel. But, not eating is a way of expressing all kinds of emotions – including anger.

Here are some guidelines you could check out, which may help you to express how you feel.

- If someone upsets you, hurts you, or even just irritates you, try to say so, *directly*. You don't have to be rude, but saying straightaway 'What you said/did just then hurt my feelings/annoyed me', is far better than bottling it up, or just dropping hints so that other people may not understand how you feel. Try to be direct and express your feelings *at the time*.
- Don't try to blame other people for how you feel. They are *your* feelings! The way you respond to other people's behaviour is up to you as an individual. What really matters is that you own these feelings and find a way of expressing them. So, whether it's anger, frustration, annoyance, hurt, or anything else . . . it's OK to feel that way. For example, you can say to someone: 'When you do so-and-so I get really annoyed'. This is far more effective and assertive than saying 'When you do so-and-so you make me annoyed'! Someone else doesn't *make* you, you *are* annoyed. That's fine, that's good. Don't try to deny it.
- Expressing anger in a physical way can help you to feel better. You can't go around hitting people but you can punch cushions which really does help to release some bottled-up tension. You may also find an assertiveness training class very useful – it's worth checking with your local library to see what's available in your area, or asking at school/college for information.
- Talk directly to the person who annoyed or angered you, not to a third person. The third party may be sympathetic, but you

will probably still be left with the feelings, because the person who annoyed you won't know.

- Try not to feel guilty. You've had a lot of practice at holding back, and coming forward may take even more time and practice and could upset you at first. Learn to accept that you have a right to stand up for yourself, because you deserve the self-esteem which comes with being assertive.

Remember, anger is not constructive if you:

- bottle it up;
- deny that it even exists;
- don't direct it at the right person;
- turn it back towards yourself (i.e. by not eating, or bingeing).

Recommended book

- Dr Paul Hauck, *How To Stand Up For Yourself* (Sheldon)

20

Joy's story

I think it all started when I had to leave school and go to college. I found it hard to make friends and felt very left out. I'd been quite chubby when I was very young (about seven or eight years old) and my brother used to make fun of me. I guess I was really sensitive about it. When I went to college, I lost most of the friends I had at school and didn't think anyone wanted me as a friend. I didn't feel like studying and the college work just got on top of me. It was really my parents' idea that I went, and I felt very pressurized by them. My mum and dad weren't very happy together either so that didn't exactly help. I think I felt if I could be good at something – say music – it would make my father happy and I would get his approval. So, I started to count calories and stopped caring about my appearance. I seemed to live in the same clothes! I knew I was very unhappy, but I didn't really know what to do. I lied to my parents about my periods stopping and went down to seven stone. Nobody seemed to notice and I felt very angry. An art teacher at college took an interest in me – art seemed to be the only way I could really express myself. I lived for art, so I decided to go to art college. I met a really nice boy and we became very close, but I couldn't handle a sexual relationship. I suppose I was anorexic for about a year and also used to make myself sick after meals. I always seemed to be conscious of my weight and had very low self-esteem.

Finally, I plucked up courage and confided in my GP who was very sympathetic and started to talk things through with me. I also started to go to self-help groups which helped a lot. Sharing things with other people who understand what you're going through makes you feel you're not all alone with the problem. Finding the right person to talk to is important. I think I felt it was all my fault somehow, but when I started talking to my doctor and people in the group I realized I hadn't done anything wrong, I just needed help to get better. For me, recovering meant finding different ways of coping. Now I feel much safer to express my feelings and I feel much better about myself. I really think it's important to be able to express your anger, too, and to be more assertive. Before, I could never stand up for myself, but now I don't mind saying what I think to people! I'm with someone really loving now and that's helped me to regain confidence too.

I think being anorexic was my way of coping, but by denying myself the pleasure of eating I was also missing out on all the other things I needed. I just seemed to push them all away together with the food I wouldn't eat. Confiding in someone was definitely the turning point for me. Now I feel I have choices which anorexia never allowed me to have.

21

A way forward

Here are some other checkpoints you may find useful

1. Try not to panic if you experience a feeling of 'fullness' at mealtimes. Remember, it will take time to adjust to eating normally again. Gradually you will learn to trust your own feelings of hunger enough to judge how much you need to eat. To begin with, though, it's a case of allowing your body to adjust to eating more than you've been used to while anorexic. Give yourself time.

2. Try to avoid thinking of any foods as 'forbidden', because this tends to make you feel guilty, which you don't need! Obviously some foods have little nutritional value, while others are essential for a healthy, nutritious diet. It's a question of balance. In a good varied diet the occasional bit of chocolate or a biscuit or two isn't a crime. Talk to your doctor/dietician if you have any questions or worries about this. If you were vegetarian before becoming anorexic, discuss this too, but be honest about it. If you're not, you will only be cheating yourself.

3. If you've been weighing yourself every day – or more often – try very hard to recognize that this too has been part of your anorexic behaviour. It may be difficult for you to let go of this habit altogether to begin with, but ideally you should leave the weighing to your doctor or hospital. At the very least, start by trying to cut down so that you're not weighing yourself every day.

4. You may find it helpful to write down your thoughts and feelings at the end of each day in a special diary or notebook. If you're not used to doing this it may seem quite difficult to begin with, but try to persevere because it will gradually become easier to do.

While you are anorexic you will undoubtedly be keeping a very strict check on your diet, maybe to the extent that you make a note of every single mouthful you eat every day. Try very hard to recognize this as being part of the behaviour you've adopted which limits all your thoughts around food, giving yourself little, if any, opportunity to think about anything else. So, instead, try to concentrate on other feelings and emotions which you begin to notice, especially if you know they are making you afraid or unable to eat, or if they perhaps make you want to binge.

One idea I think is a useful way of getting directly in touch with your feelings – particularly when you are experiencing anxiety – is to write down in a notebook, these two questions:
– How do I feel?
– What do I need?

Because you may have pushed your feelings and needs aside for quite some time, try not to blame yourself or feel guilty if the answers to these questions don't immediately come to you. Take some time for yourself to sit and think about it. If nothing comes to mind straightaway, please don't worry. Try again another time and, I believe, you will find it will gradually become easier. Answering these questions could well help to take your mind off your thoughts about food, calorie counting, exercising, etc. The chances are that focusing on these questions will ultimately help you to get in touch with the real, underlying problems that are causing you to punish yourself by starving.

Perhaps you would like an example of how you might answer the questions:
– 'How do I feel?'
– 'What do I need?'

Your replies could be something along the lines of:
– 'I *feel* sad.'
– 'I *need* to talk to someone who cares.'
or maybe:
– 'I *feel* lonely.'
– 'I *need* a hug.'

Make sure you write down whatever comes to mind.

The next step – the harder one – is to *act* on the 'what do I need' replies you come up with. Approaching someone you trust – confiding in them – and/or asking for a hug, may well not be easy for you at first. After all, you've denied having any needs at all – possibly for some time – so, like anything else, acknowledging what your needs are, accepting them and doing something about it could take both time and practice.

Bear in mind that denying yourself food has been your way of trying to cope with difficult feelings and situations. Therefore it stands to reason that while you are in the process of recovery and you are faced with a particular problem or emotion your first reaction may well be to stop eating. Remember, though, that this way of 'coping' *doesn't* work – so this is where (as I've suggested in checkpoint 4) writing down your thoughts and feelings can be very useful. Anytime you find something difficult, ask yourself how not eating could possibly make things better – and focus your energy on thinking about your *real* needs and feelings. Again, I emphasise this will be a gradual process. Sometimes you may have setbacks. A 'setback' is *not* a 'mistake', so please do not be disheartened . . . continue with your new ways of coping and give yourself the credit you deserve for taking steps forward.

Not all your feelings will necessarily be difficult ones though. You may feel particularly pleased with some progress you've made, or something you've learnt about yourself, so it's worth writing down anything that's important to you. Doing this will help you gradually to become more aware of the different kinds of emotions and thoughts you're experiencing.

5. Learn to relax. When you are anorexic and/or bulimic you may well be feeling anxious and tense much of the time. During the stages of recovery, it will be very helpful for you to let go of this tension – although I should add that a certain amount of stress in everyday life is normal. It is when feelings of anxiety and tension interfere with your life that you do need to find ways of coping. There are many books and cassettes, and even videos, which teach relaxation techniques. I tend to favour cassettes, because to relax effectively, I always find it is better to do so lying down, in a warm, yet well-ventilated room, with my eyes closed. So a cassette or CD, maybe with some soothing music, seems to me to be a better option. Obviously, though, you need to choose a technique that suits you.

One very simple and effective relaxation exercise is to put aside some time each day, even a quarter of an hour, at a time when you won't be disturbed, and play some gentle, soft music and get comfortable – you may prefer to sit in a chair or choose to lie down. It's up to you. Start with your feet, and working up through each part of your body – your feet, legs, arms, hands, back, stomach, buttocks, shoulders, face – tense each of the muscles by squeezing them tightly, feeling the tension, then very gently let go. Notice the difference between tense muscles and relaxed muscles before you move on to the next part of your body. You can even use this technique any time of the day if, for instance, you notice your shoulders are hunched up or if you are clenching your hands – notice the tension and then slowly let it go. Eventually, it will be something you will become more used to doing.

I think it's important not to become anxious about relaxing! Obviously, that would defeat the object, so remember, like anything else, it takes time and practice to learn how to relax. Learn in your own time and try not to set yourself unrealistic goals. Five minutes a day is better than nothing at all – increase the time you put aside for yourself at your own pace. Half an hour a day may feel right for some people, but it may be too much for you. Even if you can manage some time once a week, you will be starting to look after yourself . . . and will feel the benefits.

6. Use all the help and support available to you in finding new, more positive way of coping with your life. Be proud of any progress you make and try not to become despondent if you have days when you don't feel you're improving. It's unrealistic to expect an over-night change: things will *gradually* improve.

A way forward

I hope this book may have helped you to understand more about anorexia. Just as importantly, I hope it has helped you to understand a little more about yourself. As I pointed out at the beginning, I haven't attempted to offer 'miracle cures', or to wave a magic wand. Recovering from anorexia involves a gradual process of acknowledging, accepting, understanding and moving forward to a different, much better place.

When you become anorexic, you invariably feel you are in control, but I hope you can now see that, on the contrary, anorexia controls *you* and takes away a great deal of your freedom – freedom to make decisions, to make your choices in life, to meet your needs.

It's really difficult to go through life completely avoiding outside pressures. But, if you can value yourself as an individual – as someone who deserves to be both healthy and happy, and not constantly compare yourself unfavourably with others, or with a so-called 'ideal', it will become so much easier to cope.

Life invariably has its up and downs and sometimes things don't go the way we want them to. These things can be very frustrating, difficult, maybe even painful and disappointing . . . certainly challenging. But, starving yourself won't ever resolve these problems. Trying to confront problems instead of blaming and harming yourself, acknowledging your needs and not allowing others to undermine your confidence, will help you to feel more in control of your life. Seeking out help and support means that you care enough about yourself to make things better.

As Joy says in her story, recovery is all about finding *new* ways of coping. Ways that don't include punishing yourself – ways of learning how to love and value yourself.

I hope you will look for and find these ways.

How to find help

Contacts for help

- *Eating Disorders Association*

Sackville Place
44 Magdalen Street
Norwich
Norfolk NR3 1JE
Helplines: Tel. 01603–621414 Monday–Friday, 4 p.m. – 6 p.m.
Special youthline helpline, Monday–Friday, 4 p.m. – 6 p.m.
Tel. 01603–765050
The Eating Disorders Association is a nationwide organization which aims to offer help and advice to sufferers and their families. They offer a sympathetic telephone helpline, reply to letters, run self-help groups, and send out newsletters, give information, resources, support and advice. Write or phone for full details.

- *Anorexia and Bulimia Care*

15 Fernhurst Gate
Aughton
Lancashire
Tel. 01695–422479/35318

or

'Arisaig'
Back Lane
Monks Eleigh
Suffolk IP7 7BA
Tel. 01449–740145

Write to the nearest address to you. This is a Christian organization which aims to help and support people with anorexia/bulimia. However, it's not necessary to have Christian beliefs in order to contact them and they won't discriminate. If you are particularly interested in the Christian aspect, the only difference is that the information you receive will include special quotes from the Bible. If you're not interested in this aspect, you will simply receive straight-forward information sheets. Anorexia and Bulimia Care can provide a list of resources, help sheets, tapes and books, including a recommended booklist.

- *Samaritans*
  Listed in local tel. directory, or ring directory enquiries or the operator.
  This is a 24-hour helpline, so you can ring anytime if you need to talk to someone. The Samaritans listen in a non-judgemental way and can offer support. You don't have to wait until you are desperate to ring them – if you feel isolated, depressed or unhappy and need to share this with someone understanding, you will find the Samaritans very sympathetic.
- *Childline*
  0800–1111 FREE 24 hours a day
  This is a 24-hour confidential helpline especially for young people. If you are in any kind of trouble, need help, or simply need support and someone to talk to, Childline can help you. Because many young people contact this number, it can sometimes be difficult to get through straight away. But, if you keep trying, sooner or later you'll get a free line, so it's worth persevering. Remember, you don't have to say any more about yourself than you feel prepared – or comfortable – to say, so there's no need to feel under pressure about this.
- *Careline*
  0181–514 1177
  Confidential, sympathetic helpline for all young people.
- *Bristol Crisis Service For Women*
  PO Box 654
  Bristol BS99 1XH
  Tel. 01272–251119 Fridays/Saturdays 9 p.m. – 12.30 p.m.
  Aims to give help and support to girls/women who harm themselves by cutting, suffer from anorexia, or are victims of sexual abuse.
- *Asian Women's Resource Centre*
  Tel. 0181–961 6547
  Sympathetic and confidential helpline.
- *NAYPCAS – National Association of Young People's Counselling and Advisory Service*
  17–23 Albion Street
  Leicester LE1 6GD
  This is not a counselling service in itself, but a service which

can provide you with details of your nearest youth counselling and advisory service. Free and confidential – send an s.a.e. for information.

- *Brook Advisory Centres*
  Central Office
  153a East Street
  London SE17 2SD
  Tel. 0171–708 1234 for your nearest Centre.
  Brook Centres are in eight cities throughout the country. They offer free confidential advice and counselling on contraception, pregnancy testing, unplanned pregnancy, infection testing or referral, and abortion referral. Brook Centres are friendly, sympathetic and non-judgemental. Their aim is to provide information and support to help young people make decisions, without any pressure or being told what to do. Girls and boys are welcome, either together or separately. Some very helpful publications are also available. Brook also runs a national 24-hour confidential helpline on 071–410 0420, offering advice on contraception, pregnancy, abortion and sexually transmitted diseases.
- *Family Planning Association Clinics*
  27–35 Mortimer Street
  London W1N 7RJ
  Tel. 0171–636 7866 for your nearest clinic.
  Free personal and confidential advice (11 a.m. – 3 p.m. weekdays) on up-to-date information about contraception, sexuality, periods, etc.
- *Saneline*
  0171–724 8000 2 p.m. – Midnight every day of the year
  A helpline where you can talk in confidence about any worries you have about an eating disorder – or any difficult feelings you may have.

Recommended books

As well as the books mentioned in each section, here are some suggestions of books you may find helpful.

- Roger Slade, *The Anorexia Nervosa Reference Book* (Harper & Row)
  Direct and clear questions and answers – a comprehensive reference book.
- Steven Levenkron, *The Best Little Girl in the World* (Puffin)
  Fictional story about a teenage girl suffering from anorexia.
- Susan Kano, *Never Diet Again* (available direct from the Eating Disorders Association)
  All about healthy eating and good living – emphasis on how to keep your diet in balance, whether or not you choose to eat meat.
- Anne Dickson, *A Woman In Your Own Right* (Quartet)
  Looks at ways of being assertive, expressing anger, saying 'No'. (If you are male reading this book, *A Woman In Your Own Right* could help you to understand how many women feel and so help you to define yourself.)
- Dr Phyllis Shaw, *Meeting People Is Fun: How To Overcome Shyness* (Sheldon)
  Supportive self-help to gain self-confidence
- Ann Mitchell, *When Parents Split Up – Divorce Explained to Young People* (Chambers)
  Sympathetic and straightforward.
- Judy Blume, *It's Not the End of the World* (Piper)
  Fictional. About coping with parents divorcing.
- Dr Paul Hauck, *How to Stand up for Yourself* (Sheldon)
  Self-help on how to become more assertive and make a stand for yourself without taking advantage of others.
- J D Salinger, *The Catcher in the Rye* (Penguin)
  This is a book I read over and over again in my teens. Funny yet moving account of an adolescent's feelings, thoughts and relationships.
- Susan Albertson, *Between the Lines* (Armada)
  Fiction. How two friends gradually realize that friendship doesn't have to end with growing up.
- Jane Dowdeswell, *Sisters on Sisters* (Thorsons)
  Sisters talk about themselves, each other and the whole range

of feelings they experience towards one another, including affection, loathing, envy, friendship and loyalty.

- Dr David Bennett, *Growing Pains* (Thorsons)
  Helps parents and children develop a better understanding of each other.
- Sue Sharpe, *Voices From Home: Girls talk about their families* (Virago Upstarts)
- Carol Weston, *Girltalk* (Pan Horizons)
  All the things your sister never told you . . . Really chatty advice and information about relationships, school, studying, sex, growing up, etc.
- John Hart, *So You Think You're Attracted to the Same Sex* (Penguin)
  A sympathetic discussion about gay and lesbian sex.
- Ouaine Bain and Maureen Sanders, *Out In the Open* (Virago Upstarts)
  A guide for young people who've been sexually abused.
- Rosemary Stones, *More to Life than Mr Right* (Lyons Tracks)
  Learning to be an independent woman in your own right.
- Dr Paul Hauck, *How to Be Your Own Best Friend* (Sheldon)
- Jill Dawson, *How Do I Look?* (Virago)
  Young women talk about their changing bodies, media images, feelings of self-image, sexuality, identity and being an individual.
- Kay Wellings, *First Love First Sex: A practical guide to relationships* (Thorsons)
  Clear comprehensive guide to all aspects of intimate and sexual relationships, with illustrations.
- Miriam Stoppard, *Every Girl's Life Guide* (Dorling Kindersley)
  Chatty and informal, dealing with lots of aspects of growing up, both physically and emotionally.
- Oralee Wachter, *No More Secrets For Me* (Penguin, 1986)
  Four easy to read stories about how very young people, threatened by invasion of privacy and sexual advances, tell a responsible adult.

- Jacqueline Roy, *Fat Chance* (1994)
  A novel written for young teenagers explaining the issues around an eating disorder and friendship. A good read.
- Pete Sanders and Steve Myers, *Let's Discuss Anorexia and Bulimia* (Watts, 1995)
  Written for both children and young teenagers to read alone or together.
- Julia Tugendhat, *Divorce – What Teenagers Tell Us About Divorce and Stepfamilies* (Bloomsbury, 1990)
  Teenagers from a variety of backgrounds share their experience of marital conflict, divorce and stepfamilies.
- Sue Sharpe, *Know Your Rights* (Collins, 1992)
  A useful guide to your rights and the law for young people. Helpful information and advice on where you stand in everyday situations.
- Joan Lingard, *Strangers in the House* (Red Fox, 1991)
  A novel for young teenagers about two families learning to adjust when the parents re-marry.
- Karen Bryant-Mole, *What's Happening? Splitting up* (Wayland, 1992)
  Answers lots of questions concerning when parents split up.
- Helena Wilkinson, *Beyond Chaotic Eating* (HarperCollins)
- Karen Bryant-Mole, *What's Happening? Bullying* (Wayland 1992)
  Answers the questions: Why am I being bullied? Should I tell? Who can I turn to? Is it my fault? What if *I'm* a Bully?

Index